THE 2:7 SERIES

COURSE 2

*"Rooted and built up in Him,
strengthened in the faith as you were taught,
and overflowing with thankfulness."*
COLOSSIANS 2:7

THE GROWING DISCIPLE

NAVPRESS

A MINISTRY OF THE NAVIGATORS
P.O. BOX 35001, COLORADO SPRINGS, COLORADO 80935

© 1979 by The Navigators
Revised edition © 1987
All rights reserved. No part of this publication may be reproduced in any form without written permission from NavPress, P.O. Box 35001, Colorado Springs, CO 80935.
ISBN: 08910-9167X

Seventh printing, 1994

Unless otherwise identified, Scripture quotations are from the *Holy Bible: New International Version*. Copyright © 1973, 1978, 1984, International Bible Society. Used by permission of Zondervan Bible Publishers; Other versions quoted are *The Amplified New Testament* (AMP), © The Lockman Foundation 1954, 1958, used by permission; *The Modern Language Bible: The Berkeley Version in Modern English* (MLB), © 1945, 1959, 1969 by Zondervan Publishing House, used by permission; the *Jerusalem Bible* (JB), © 1966, 1967, 1968 by Darton, Longman and Todd, Ltd., and Doubleday and Co., Inc., used by permission; *The Living Bible* (LB), © 1971 by Tyndale House Publishers, Wheaton, Illinois, used by permission; The *New American Standard Bible* (NASB), © The Lockman Foundation 1960, 1962, 1963, 1968, 1971, 1972, 1973, 1975, 1977; *The New English Bible* (NEB), © the Delegates of the Oxford University Press and the Syndics of the Cambridge University Press, 1961, 1970, reprinted by permission; J. B. Phillips; *The New Testament in Modern English, Revised Edition* (PH), © J. B. Phillips, 1958, 1960, 1972, published by the Macmillan Company, New York, and Collins Publishers, London, used by permission; the *Revised Standard Version of the Bible* (RSV), copyrighted 1946, 1952, © 1971, 1973; the *Good News Bible* New Testament (GNB), © American Bible Society, 1966, 1971, 1976; Kenneth S. Wuest: *Wuest Word Studies from the Greek New Testament* (WUEST), © 1942, 1947, 1952, 1954, by Wm. B. Eerdmans Publishing Company; and the *King James Version* (KJV).

Printed in the United States of America

Important

PARTICIPANTS

This course is designed to be used *only* by those who have successfully completed *Growing Strong in God's Family* and Course 1 in *The 2:7 Series*.

LEADERS

Courses in *The 2:7 Series* should be *led only* by qualified leaders who have *participated in an instructor training* clinic. Clinics are available to churches and individuals desiring access to this discipleship curriculum. Information regarding training clinics may be obtained from Church Discipleship Ministries, The Navigators, P.O. Box 6000, Colorado Springs, CO 80934. The telephone number is (719) 598-1212.

Comprehensive leaders guides have been prepared for those leading groups in *The 2:7 Series*. The leaders guides are available only to those who have attended a training clinic.

ACKNOWLEDGMENT

We are grateful for the dedicated efforts of Ron Oertli who originated the concept of *Growing Strong in God's Family* and *The 2:7 Series* and is their principal author.

Contents

Bible Reading Highlights Records and Prayer sheets are included following page 78.

Completion Record

Ask others in your study group to check you on your completion of the requirements in this course and have them initial and date each section.

SCRIPTURE MEMORY	Initial	Date
Proclaim Christ, TMS **B** 1-12, memory verses:		
"All Have Sinned" — Romans 3:23		
"All Have Sinned" — Isaiah 53:6		
"Sin's Penalty" — Romans 6:23		
"Sin's Penalty" — Hebrews 9:27		
"Christ Paid the Penalty" — Romans 5:8		
"Christ Paid the Penalty" — I Peter 3:18		
"Salvation Not by Works" — Ephesians 2:8-9		
"Salvation Not by Works" — Titus 3:5		
"Must Receive Christ" — John 1:12		
"Must Receive Christ" — Romans 10:9-10		
"Assurance of Salvation" — I John 5:13		
"Assurance of Salvation" — John 5:24		
Quoted all of *Proclaim Christ*, **B** 1-12		
Reviewed all of *Live the New Life*, **A** 1-12 for 14 consecutive days		
Reviewed all of *Beginning with Christ* for 14 consecutive days		

QUIET TIME		
Completed *Bible Reading Highlights Record* for 14 consecutive days		

EVANGELISM		
Identified with Christ in a relating activity (page 15)		
Completed "Relationship Evangelism Bible Study" (pages 29-31)		
Testimony given without notes in less than 4 minutes		
Used Evangelism Prayer List for 7 consecutive days		
Gave *The Bridge Illustration*:		
Outline		
Role played		
To someone outside of 2:7 group		

BIBLE STUDY		
Session 3—"The Call to Fruitful Living" (pages 21-27)		
Session 5—"Love in Action" (pages 33-37)		

Session 6—"Purity of Life" (pages 39-44)		
Session 8—"Integrity in Living" (pages 52-56)		
Session 11—"Character in Action" (pages 71-77)		

OTHER

Meditation exercise (pages 10-15)		
Completed Matthew 6:33 study (pages 58-61)		
Completed "Priorities—Part I" (pages 61-65)		
Studied "Priorities—Part II" (pages 66-70)		

LEADER'S CHECK

Graduated from Course 2		

Session 1

OUTLINE OF THIS SESSION:
1. Go over "Review the Goals of Course 1" (page 7).
2. Preview Course 2 by looking over the *Completion Record* (pages 5-6).
3. Survey the "Scripture Memory Instructions—Week One" (page 8).
4. Read "The Topical Memory System in This Course" (pages 9-10).
5. Do parts 1 and 2 of the group exercise "How to Meditate on the Scriptures" (pages 10-15).
   a. Write out a paraphrase of 2 Timothy 3:16.
   b. Ask yourself questions on Hebrews 10:24-25.
6. Discuss current use of the Evangelism Prayer List.
7. Read and discuss "Openly Identifying with Christ" (pages 15-16).
8. Read the "Assignment for Session 2" (page 16).
9. Close the session in prayer.

Review the Goals of Course 1

The goals of Course 1 were:
1. To experience a more consistent and meaningful quiet time by . . .
   a. combining meaningful Bible reading and prayer.
   b. succeeding in having 14 consecutive quiet times during the course.
   c. recording daily quiet time thoughts and how they impressed you on a *Bible Reading Highlights Record.*
   d. growing in your ability to share key quiet time thoughts with others in the group.
2. To quote accurately the five Scripture memory verses of *Beginning with Christ* (the five Assurance verses).
3. To memorize the first 12 verses of the *Topical Memory System* successfully. (These 12 verses are correlated with *The Wheel Illustration*.)
4. To study and discuss the booklet *My Heart Christ's Home.*
5. To have a half day of prayer after reading and discussing the article *How to Spend a Day in Prayer.*
6. To complete and discuss five studies as a participant in a Bible study group.
7. To give a personal salvation testimony in less than four minutes, using notes from a 3″ x 5″ card.
8. To relate with a non-Christian friend through a non-spiritual activity.

7

Scripture Memory Instructions—Week One
From the *Topical Memory System*

You're Under Way . . .

You're off to a good start, having completed the first unit of the *Topical Memory System* (**A** 1-12) in Course 1. You have begun to enjoy some of the benefits Scripture memory can bring. Now keep up your momentum as you tackle the next 12 verses (**B** 1-12).

Study these instructions, then each week read the comments *About the Verses* and follow the instructions in the section *Your Weekly Plan*.

What to Expect

Scripture memory can help us in three major areas—witnessing effectively, overcoming anxiety, and having victory in temptation. In Course 2 you will learn 12 verses which will greatly contribute to your effectiveness in witnessing.

Use the Buddy System

The Scriptures teach that "as iron sharpens iron, so one man sharpens another" (Proverbs 27:17), and, "Two are better than one . . . . If one falls down, his friend can help him up" (Ecclesiastes 4:9-10). We all need encouragement in our Christian lives and this surely applies to memorizing Scripture.

Ask someone else in your 2:7 group to get together with you outside class to help you review your verses. You may also want to talk over any difficulties you are having, but *above all share how God is using the verses in your lives*. This will help you succeed in Scripture memory.

Knowledge and Application

Some Christians confuse Bible knowledge with spiritual maturity, assuming that knowing more about the Bible automatically makes them better Christians. This is not necessarily true. The Pharisees knew the Old Testament, yet they were spiritually blind. The key to spiritual maturity is sincere application of God's Word to life.

The Apostle Paul addressed the Corinthian believers as fleshly, unspiritual babes in Christ. He had to feed them milk instead of solid spiritual food. They took pride in their wisdom and logic, and could have understood the deeper truths Paul wanted to impart to them. But their lives contradicted what they professed to believe. Jealousy and strife split their ranks and they behaved like ordinary, unregenerate men. Their lives were too much like those of the unbelievers in Corinth. What an indictment! They needed to apply the Word of God to their daily living.

Visualize the Verse

We remember pictures more easily than words or concepts. If you find it difficult to connect a particular verse with its topic and reference, try forming a mental picture of the verse based on its content, context, or some other feature that will help you remember. The picture can become the mental hook you use later to draw the verse from your memory. It helps if you make the image as unusual or striking as possible.

For example, consider the verses in Course 1 on witnessing, Matthew 4:19 and Romans 1:16. Associate the first verse with Christ and the second with Paul. Picture Jesus standing on a beach by the Sea of Galilee. Two fishermen are tending their nets when He calls out, "Come, follow me, and I will make you fishers of men." Fix this scene in your mind. Associate the picture with the topic of witnessing and with the reference Matthew 4:19.

Paul didn't write the book of Romans from Rome, but since it was addressed to the believers there, you might picture Paul standing in the Roman Forum or Colosseum speaking out to the pagan citizens, "I am not ashamed of the gospel, because it is the power of God for the salvation of everyone who believes: first for the Jew, then for the Gentile". Associate this picture with the topic of witnessing and with the reference Romans 1:16.

Visualizing a verse is especially helpful if you find it difficult to remember by ordinary means.

Self-checking Quiz

A self-checking quiz on these instructions, as well as your weekly memory work, will be taken in Course 3.

The Topical Memory System *in This Course*

You have already learned the first 12 verses of the *Topical Memory System*, which make up series **A.** *Live the New Life.* The four remaining series are **B.** *Proclaim Christ;* **C.** *Be Christ's Disciple;* **D.** *Grow in Christlikeness;* and **E.** *Rely on God's Resources.* In Course 2 you will memorize the second 12 verses, which include key Scriptures to use in explaining the gospel to others:

B. *Proclaim Christ*

All have Sinned	Romans 3:23	Isaiah 53:6
Sin's Penalty	Romans 6:23	Hebrews 9:27
Christ Paid the Penalty	Romans 5:8	1 Peter 3:18
Salvation Not by Works	Ephesians 2:8-9	Titus 3:5
Must Receive Christ	John 1:12	Romans 10:9-10
Assurance of Salvation	1 John 5:13	John 5:24

Below are the topics and references for the memory verses you have already learned in *Growing Strong in God's Family* and Course 1 in *The 2:7 Series.* Plan to end Course 2 with the ability to skillfully quote each of these important 17 verses as well as the 12 verses you are learning during Course 2. You have accomplished a great deal toward memorizing God's Word and having it available to use in your own life and for helping others.

From *Beginning with Christ*:

Assurance of Salvation	1 John 5:11-12
Assurance of Answered Prayer	John 16:24
Assurance of Victory	1 Corinthians 10:13
Assurance of Forgiveness	1 John 1:9
Assurance of Guidance	Proverbs 3:5-6

A. *Live the New Life*

Christ the Center	2 Corinthians 5:17	Galatians 2:20
Obedience to Christ	Romans 12:1	John 14:21
The Word	2 Timothy 3:16	Joshua 1:8
Prayer	John 15:7	Philippians 4:6-7
Fellowship	1 John 1:3	Hebrews 10:24-25
Witnessing	Matthew 4:19	Romans 1:16

MEDITATION—AN AID TO APPLICATION

One of the most beneficial reasons for memorizing Scripture verses is that it stimulates us to meditate on their contents. During this course you will be doing an exercise (pages 10-15) to increase your ability to meditate on passages of Scripture.

An important part of your Scripture memory program should be meditating on verses you have learned. Not only will this enable you to retain them in your memory with accuracy, but as you reflect on and consider their contents, you will experience challenges, encouragement, and motivation. Remember God's instruction to Joshua: "Do not let this Book of the law depart from your mouth; meditate on it day and night, so that you may be careful to do everything written in it. Then you will be prosperous and successful" (Joshua 1:8).

IMPORTANCE OF DAILY REVIEW

Continual review is the key to having a grasp on the verses you already have learned. An excellent goal you could establish would be to know your memory verses so well by the end of Course 2 that you can not only quote them accurately, but also quickly list the specific topics under Series A and Series B, as well as for the *Beginning with Christ* verses. Plan not only to complete your memory assignments each week in Course 2, but also to daily quote the topics and references of all the verses you have learned.

Scripture memory and meditation is a strategic part of the discipleship training in which you are involved. It promotes your spiritual development and lays the foundation for future spiritual growth. You will then agree with the psalmist: "Oh, how I love your law! I meditate on it all day long" (Psalm 119:97).

How to Meditate on the Scriptures
A Group Exercise

"Blessed is the man
  who does not walk in the counsel of the wicked
or stand in the way of sinners
  or sit in the seat of mockers.
But his delight is in the law of the LORD,
  and on his law he meditates day and night.
He is like a tree planted by streams of water,
  which yields its fruit in season
and whose leaf does not wither.
Whatever he does prospers."

—Psalm 1:1-3

WHAT IS MEDITATION?

Meditation is the act of reflecting on, pondering, musing over, or contemplating. Meditation is *not* mind-wandering or indulging in "mental drifting," but it has form and an object. Bible verses and scriptural concepts are the focus of a Christian's meditation.

When we meditate, we spend a few moments *directing* our thoughts to a single object or subject. Meditation is thinking with a purpose.

Meditation is *not* a solemn, academic exercise. It requires an attitude of curiosity and expectation leading to exciting discoveries, refreshment of spirit, and transformation of character. It brings reward and benefit.

When we meditate, we purposefully sort through information for clarification, for application, for categorization, and for assimilation.

FURTHER INSIGHT INTO MEDITATION

> *"This book of the Law must never depart from your mouth; you must meditate on it day and night, so that you may keep living in accord with all that is written in it; for then you will make your way successful, and then you will prosper."*
>
> —Joshua 1:8 (BERK)

During this class session you will have opportunity to practice two methods of meditation (1 and 2, on pages 11-13). As part of your homework for next week, you will practice four additional methods of meditation (3-6, pages 14-15).

1—Paraphrase

The first method of meditation you will practice is to write a paraphrase. As you attempt to put a verse or passage into your own words, you will understand it more clearly. Some exciting insights can come from writing your own paraphrase.

On the lines on page 12 write out 2 Timothy 3:16 in your own words, using the scriptures on page 11 to help you complete this part of your work. (You may want to use more words in your paraphrase than are in the original verse.)

VARIOUS TRANSLATIONS AND PARAPHRASES OF 2 TIMOTHY 3:16

"All Scripture is God-breathed and is useful for teaching, rebuking, correcting and training in righteousness" (NIV).

"All Scripture is given by inspiration of God, and is profitable for doctine, for reproof, for correction, for instruction in righteousness" (NKJV).

"All Scripture is inspired by God and profitable for teaching, for reproof, for correction, for training in righteousness" (NASB).

"For all Scripture is inspired by God and is useful for teaching the truth, rebuking error, correcting faults, and giving instruction for right living" (TEV).

"All Scripture is inspired by God and profitable for teaching, for reproof, for correction, and for training in righteousness" (RSV).

"All Scripture is inspired by God and can profitably be used for teaching, for refuting error, for guiding people's lives and teaching them to be holy" (JB).

"Every Scripture is God-breathed—given by His inspiration—and profitable for instruction, for reproof and conviction of sin, for correction of error and discipline in obedience, and for training in righteousness [that is, in holy living, in conformity to God's will in thought, purpose, and action]" (AMP).

A PARAPHRASE OF 2 TIMOTHY 3:16

_____

_____

_____

_____

_____

_____

_____

_____

_____

_____

_____

_____

_____

_____

_____

_____

2—Questions

A second method of meditation to practice now is to ask yourself questions about a verse. You may use two possible methods in asking yourself questions. You may use the *who, what, when, where, why,* and *how* questions, or you may jot down random questions which come to mind as you reflect on the passage. You may not come up with answers immediately for all your questions.

On the lines on page 13 jot down some of the questions and answers that come to mind as you meditate on Hebrews 10:24-25, using the scriptures below to help you. Begin by asking who, what, where, when, why, or how, or use random questions.

VARIOUS TRANSLATIONS AND PARAPHRASES OF HEBREWS 10:24-25

"Let us consider how we may spur one another on toward love and good deeds. Let us not give up meeting together, as some are in the habit of doing, but let us encourage one another—and all the more as you see the Day approaching" (NIV).

"And let us consider one another in order to stir up love and good works, not forsaking the assembling of ourselves together, as is the manner of some, but exhorting one another, and so much the more as you see the Day approaching" (NKJV).

"And let us consider how to stimulate one another to love and good deeds, not forsaking our own assembling together, as is the habit of some, but encouraging *one another*; and all the more, as you see the day drawing near" (NASB).

"Let us be concerned for one another, to help one another to show love and to do good. Let us not give up the habit of meeting together, as some are doing. Instead, let us encourage one another all the more, since you see that the Day of the Lord is coming nearer." (TEV).

"And let us consider how to stir up one another to love and good works, not neglecting to meet together, as is the habit of some, but encouraging one another, and all the more as you see the Day drawing near" (RSV).

"Let us be concerned for each other, to stir a response in love and good works. Do not stay away from the meetings of the community, as some do, but encourage each other to go; the more so as you see the Day drawing near" (JB).

"And let us consider *and* give attentive, continuous care to watching over one another, studying how we may stir up (stimulate and incite) to love *and* helpful deeds *and* noble activities; not forsaking or neglecting to assemble together (as believers), as is the habit of some people, but admonishing—warning, urging, and encouraging—one another, and all the more faithfully as you see the day approaching" (AMP).

QUESTIONS ABOUT HEBREWS 10:24-25

3—Prayer

Pray over the verse or passage. One way to do this is to think about each phrase or thought and pray about the implications for your life or for the lives of others. *The best things I prayed about while meditating on Romans 12:1 were*:

_____

_____

_____

_____

_____

_____

_____

_____

4—Emphasis

Emphasize different words or phrases. Read or quote a verse aloud several times and stress a different word or phrase each time. This puts your focus on various facets. Each word adds its own significance to the passage. *The best thoughts I had while emphasizing different words in John 15:7 were*:

_____

_____

_____

_____

_____

_____

5—Cross-reference

Find cross-references. Using a concordance or other Bible study aid, find additional verses which support the basic concept of the passage you are cross-referencing. *Other verses which say the same things as John 14:21 are*:

Reference _____ Thought _____

_____

_____

Reference _____ Thought _____

_____

_____

_____

6—Application

Seek to make an application. Prayerfully reflect on the passage allowing God to show you how to apply its truths. Try to make your application a positive, specific step you will take. *In considering how Philippians 4:6-7 relates to my own circumstances, I had some of the following thoughts:*

_____

_____

_____

_____

_____

_____

Openly Identifying with Christ

During Course 1 you had an assignment to participate in at least one "non-spiritual" activity with a non-Christian. Since then you have probably been involved in several activities with one or more non-Christians. As you know, spending time together is the primary way in which you develop friendship and openness with someone.

During Course 2 you are required to openly identify with Christ when you are with a non-Christian acquaintance. Some call this "flying the flag". Old sailing ships flew the flag of their country so they could be identified from a distance by another ship. They were "flying the flag" of the sovereign and country for whom they held allegiance. There is a point when a Christian needs to verbally begin "flying the flag".

To openly identify with Christ does not mean to give your complete testimony or share the gospel. It simply means that you make a statement or comment that identifies you with Christ. It is wise to prepare what you might like to say when you have the opportunity. You could refer to something you heard in a sermon at church or something your child heard in Sunday school. You could refer to something Christ said in one of the gospels. You could make a brief statement about praying for someone or something. Be direct enough to be understood. Be confident, yet gentle. Never sound defensive. Be low-key.

> *"And the Lord's servant must not quarrel; instead, he must be kind to everyone, able to teach, not resentful. Those who oppose him he must gently instruct, in the hope that God will grant them repentance leading them to a knowledge of the truth."*
> —II Timothy 2:24-25

It is good to identify with Christ early in a relationship. The longer you go in the relationship without identifying with Christ, the harder it will be to share your faith with that person. Pray for wisdom and boldness, make a plan, then carry it out in a gracious manner.

You may remember the interesting conversation between God and Jeremiah in Jeremiah 1:6-8. Jeremiah spoke first.—"'Ah, Sovereign LORD,' I said, 'I do not know how to speak; I am only a child.' But the LORD said to me, 'Do not say, "I am only a child." You must go to everyone I send you to and say whatever I command you. Do not be afraid of them, for I am with you and will rescue you,' declares the LORD."—You, too, may sometimes feel fearful or uneasy, but God will give you the courage and wisdom to say what needs to be said. Later you can build on this brief spiritual conversation.

ASSIGNMENT FOR SESSION 2:

1. Scripture Memory: Study and complete the "Scripture Memory Instructions—Week Two" (pages 17-18). Memorize the two verses on "All Have Sinned," Romans 3:23 and Isaiah 53:6.
2. Quiet Time: Continue your Bible reading, marking, and recording, and using your Prayer sheets.
3. Evangelism: Come to class prepared to give your personal testimony without notes in less than four minutes.
4. Other: Complete meditation methods 3-6 (pages 14-15). Meditation should not be hurried; take your time and enjoy the exercises.

Session 2

OUTLINE OF THIS SESSION:

1. Break into verse review groups and review the two verses on "All Have Sinned," Romans 3:23 and Isaiah 53:6. (Work at getting anything signed that you can on your *Completion Record*.)
2. Share some quiet time thoughts from your *Bible Reading Highlights Record*.
3. Discuss methods 3-6 in your meditation exercises (pages 14-15).
4. Have two or three people give a personal testimony without notes in less than four minutes.
5. Read "Introduction to Bible Study—Course 2" (pages 18-19).
6. Read the "Assignment for Session 3" (page 19).
7. Close the session in prayer.

Scripture Memory Instructions—Week Two

And Now to Continue . . .

In the second series you again have three things to work with each week:

1. *Your memory materials*—12 verse cards on the subject *Proclaim Christ*. You will use the same vinyl verse pack you used in *Growing Strong in God's Family* and in Course 1. (Don't put all the new cards in the pack at once. Keep them in a convenient place where they will be accessible each week.)

2. *Comments about the verses*—to help you understand and apply the Scriptures as you learn them.

3. *Your weekly plan*—to help you progress steadily and avoid pitfalls in your daily memory program.

About the Verses

SERIES **B**. PROCLAIM CHRIST

As witnesses for Jesus Christ we have two things to share—*our testimony* of how we found Christ and what He means to us, and *the gospel*, God's plan of salvation. The gospel includes the facts of people's need, God's love for people, and

what He did to meet that need.

The topics and verses in this series form a usable outline for presenting the gospel. They will help you become more skillful in proclaiming Christ.

TOPIC 1. ALL HAVE SINNED

Today's complex world faces seemingly insurmountable problems of war, crime, racial strife, and violence of all kinds. Experts search desperately for solutions, but few acknowledge the basic cause. Christ, however, went to the root of the matter. He said that envy, pride, impurity, immorality, theft, murder, and wickedness are merely results of the real problem—our sinful hearts (Mark 7:20-23). People will never find a solution to their problems until they agree with God's diagnosis of the cause—sin.

Romans 3:23—The passage around this verse informs us that there is no distinction among people: Both Jews and Gentiles have sinned and fallen short of God's standard of righteousness. Everyone is in the same situation.

Note: Occasionally, in order to focus attention on a particular thought, you will memorize a verse that is not a complete sentence. This is another reason why you should read the context of the verses you memorize.

Isaiah 53:6—Isaiah stated that everyone has willfully turned his back on God, preferring to go his own way. The Bible allows no exception to this (see Romans 3:10-12). Every human is infected by sin.

Your Weekly Plan

1. At the beginning of the week make sure the 12 verses of Series **A** are inside your verse pack with the five *Beginning with Christ* verses.

2. Now place the first two verses of Series **B** (Romans 3:23 and Isaiah 53:6) in the window on the outside of your pack. Keep the remaining verses in a place where they will be accessible each week.

Each part of your pack has a distinct function. If you have a verse pack with an outside window, the window can be used for learning your new verses, and the inside of the pack to review and maintain the verses you have already memorized.

3. Each day review the 17 verses on the inside of your pack (Series **A** and the *Beginning with Christ* verses).

4. Reread the steps on "How to Memorize a Verse Effectively" in the *Growing Strong in God's Family* workbook (page 13). If, for example, your 2:7 class meets on Sunday, learn the first verse on Monday and Tuesday. As soon as you can, say it at least once without looking, then repeat it frequently throughout Monday and Tuesday to fix it firmly in mind.

5. Follow the same steps with the second verse on Wednesday and Thursday and review the first. Review both verses on Friday and Saturday.

6. By the end of the week write out your two new verses from memory or quote them to someone to make sure you have learned them correctly.

Introduction to Bible Study—Course 2

Having completed *Growing Strong in God's Family* and the first course in *The 2:7 Series*, you have undoubtedly deepened your convictions about the profit of personal Bible study—what it means to search the Scriptures and discover truth. You have probably noticed that when you investigate the Word for yourself, it affects your attitudes and actions day by day.

However, even though you realize the importance of systematic Bible study, you will probably sense opposition as you continue. The enemy of every Christian, Satan himself, knows the power of God's Word, and he will try at every turn to keep you from it. You will find such excuses as, "You're too busy," or, "You can't concentrate now—do this little thing first, then get back to Bible study." You will find interruptions, temptations, and even criticism by others hindering you from giving your attention to the Scriptures.

Recognizing that Satan is the cause of such hindrances is helpful. It reemphasizes the importance of Bible study, and can increase your determination to study. How do you win? Here are some practical suggestions:

1. Accept by faith the victory that Christ has already won over Satan and all his works. "Thanks be to God! He gives us the victory through our Lord Jesus Christ" (1 Corinthians 15:57).

2. Ask the Lord for wisdom and strength. "Call to me and I will answer you and tell you great and unsearchable things you do not know" (Jeremiah 33:3).

3. Use personal discipline. No spiritual exercise becomes automatic. Just as you must make an effort to keep up your daily quiet time with the Lord, so you must plan and zealously guard your study time. It is good to set a definite goal for a certain amount of study to be completed each week and to be diligent in reaching that goal. "A longing fulfilled is sweet to the soul," Solomon said (Proverbs 13:19), and satisfaction is yours when you reach a planned objective.

4. Arrange with a friend to check you on your weekly goals in Bible study, and perhaps share something you have learned from it with him.

During Course 2 you will prepare and discuss Bible studies related to Christian character. Character has been defined as "moral excellence and firmness". God desires that we have strong, moral qualities in our inner lives as well as acceptable and effective outward behavior. Therefore, it is imperative that we learn what God's Word says about the character of the Christian. The five areas of Christian character you will study in this course are:

> The Call to Fruitful Living
> Love in Action
> Purity of Life
> Integrity in Living
> Character in Action

ASSIGNMENT FOR SESSION 3:
1. Scripture Memory: Study and complete the "Scripture Memory Instructions—Week Three" (page 20). Memorize the two verses on "Sin's Penalty," Romans 6:23 and Hebrews 9:27.
2. Quiet Time: Continue your Bible reading, marking, and recording.
3. Bible Study: Complete the Bible study, "The Call to Fruitful Living" (pages 21-27).
4. Evangelism: Come to class prepared to give your personal testimony without notes in less than four minutes.

Session 3

OUTLINE OF THIS SESSION:

1. Break into verse review groups and review the two verses on "Sin's Penalty," Romans 6:23 and Hebrews 9:27. (Work at getting anything signed that you can on your *Completion Record.*)
2. Share some quiet time thoughts from your *Bible Reading Highlights Record.*
3. Have two or three people give a personal testimony without notes in less than four minutes.
4. Discuss the Bible study, "The Call to Fruitful Living" (pages 21-27).
5. Read the "Assignment for Session 4" (page 27).
6. Have a short period of prayer for non-Christians on your Evangelism Prayer List.

Scripture Memory Instructions—Week Three

About the Verses

TOPIC 2. SIN'S PENALTY

The fact that every person is a sinner has serious consequences.

Romans 6:23—Paul said that sin results in death. All will die physically some day, but all have already died spiritually. Spiritual death is separation from God. This is why even though most people believe in the existence of God, they have no personal fellowship with Him. They are separated from Him by an impassable gulf, which is the result of sin.

God is love, but He is also just. He cannot overlook sin and remain either just or holy. The only thing a holy God can do to sin is judge it. The Bible says, "Whoever rejects the Son will not see life, for God's wrath remains on him [literally, 'hangs over his head']" (John 3:36). We may not like to think about it, but the Bible speaks as much of judgment as it does of almost any other topic. We need to know about it.

Hebrews 9:27—Every person has an appointment with death and judgment. The man without Christ cannot escape these imperatives. Everyone must give account of himself to God.

Your Weekly Plan

1. Place the next two verses of Series **B** (Romans 6:23 and Hebrews 9:27) in the window of your pack.
2. Repeat your memorized verses every day and work on learning your new verses. Learn the first one before concentrating on the second.
3. Carry your verse pack at all times and use spare moments for review.
4. By the end of the week, check yourself by writing out your new verses or quoting them to someone.

THE CALL TO FRUITFUL LIVING

Many people measure the fruitfulness of their lives by the quantity of their activities. This does not necessarily give a true picture of the quality of their lives. *What you are is more important than what you do.*

THINK ABOUT: How do you think fruitfulness is measured in the life of a Christian?

GOD'S DESIRE FOR YOUR FRUITFULNESS

1. Read John 15:5. Here Christ gives insight into the matter of spiritual fruit-bearing.

   a. In this analogy identify the vine and the branches.

   _____

   _____

   _____

   _____

   b. What condition is necessary for the branch to bear fruit?

   _____

   _____

   _____

   c. Why does the branch need the vine?

   _____

   _____

   _____

   d. Explain what you think it means to "abide" or "remain" in Christ.

   _____

   _____

   _____

2. What additional observations can you make about bearing fruit from John 15:8,16?

   _____

   _____

   _____

   _____

3. Read Galatians 5:22-23 and list the qualities God wants to produce in your life. Briefly define each one.

THE FRUIT OF THE SPIRIT	BRIEF DEFINITION OF THE FRUIT
1. _____	_____
	_____
2. _____	_____
	_____
3. _____	_____
	_____
4. _____	_____
	_____
5. _____	_____
	_____
6. _____	_____
	_____
7. _____	_____
	_____
8. _____	_____
	_____
9. _____	_____
	_____

Which of the above qualities is currently the most important to you and why?

_____

_____

_____

GROWING IN CHARACTER

4. Scripture reveals several important areas of life in which character is displayed. List one for each of the following verses.

Philippians 4:8 _____

Colossians 4:6 _____

I Peter 2:12 _____

What is the relationship between these three areas?

_____

_____

_____

_____

5. Carefully examine 2 Peter 1:1-8. This portion of Scripture deals with the subject of growth in Christian character.
   a. How has God equipped you to grow in character? Verses 2-4

   _____

   _____

   _____

   _____

   b. What does verse 8 say about fruitfulness?

   _____

   _____

   _____

   c. List eight aspects of Christian character.

   _____   _____

   _____   _____

   _____   _____

   _____   _____

   How might their sequence be significant?

   _____

   _____

   _____

   _____

   d. Choose three of these qualities and write a definition for each which adequately expresses what you understand the quality to mean.

   1. _____

   _____

   2. _____

   _____

   3. _____

   _____

e. Select one quality which you would like to strengthen. With God's help, what steps could you take to become more Christlike in displaying that quality?

_____

_____

_____

_____

_____

Sow a thought, reap an act;
Sow an act, reap a habit;
Sow a habit, reap a character;
Sow a character, reap a destiny.

GROWING IN WISDOM

6. One of the purposes of the Book of Proverbs is that people might attain wisdom. What do the following verses teach about wisdom?

Proverbs 2:6 _____

Proverbs 3:13-14 _____

Proverbs 9:10 _____

Proverbs 11:2 _____

Proverbs 24:13-14 _____

7. Read James 3:13-18.
   a. How is godly wisdom displayed?

   _____

   _____

   b. List the characteristics of godly wisdom and ungodly wisdom. Verses 15-17.

GODLY WISDOM	UNGODLY WISDOM

c. Which of the preceding characteristics have influenced our society the most? Explain your answer.

_____

_____

_____

_____

_____

_____

_____

_____

"Wisdom is more than knowledge, which is the accumulation of facts ... it is the right application of knowledge in moral and spiritual matters."

—J. Oswald Sanders

CHANGING ATTITUDES

8. Read Philippians 3:4-14.

   a. List several of Paul's new attitudes and patterns which differed from his former ones.

PAUL'S FORMER ATTITUDES AND PATTERNS (VERSES 4-7)	PAUL'S NEW ATTITUDES AND PATTERNS (VERSES 7-14)
1. Put confidence in the flesh	_____
2. Religious leader	_____
3. Persecuted the church	_____
4. Blameless in the Law	_____
5. Counted all as gain for self	_____

   b. Why do you feel Paul had such a positive attitude about the future?

_____

_____

_____

_____

_____

_____

9. In the Sermon on the Mount Jesus Christ gives eight basic ingredients for living a holy, happy life. From Matthew 5:3-12, list the blessing that He promises to the person with each quality.

KIND OF PERSON	JESUS' PROMISE
a. The poor in spirit (recognizing one's own poverty in spiritual things) Verse 3	
b. Person who mourns (is genuinely sorry for sin) Verse 4	
c. The meek (having strength under control) Verse 5	
d. Person who hungers for righteousness (deep concern for holiness) Verse 6	
e. The merciful (compassionate) Verse 7	
f. The pure in heart (free from moral sin) Verse 8	
g. The peacemaker (promotes peace by reconciling others) Verse 9	
h. The one persecuted (oppressed for Christ's sake) Verses 10-11	

10. In which one of the above areas are you currently the strongest?

_____

_____

In which one are you the weakest?

_____

_____

SUMMARY
Review the chapter subtopics and write your own summary of each section.

God's Desire for Your Fruitfulness

_____

_____

_____

_____

_____

Growing in Character

_____

_____

_____

_____

Growing in Wisdom

_____

_____

_____

_____

_____

_____

Changing Attitudes

_____

_____

_____

_____

_____

ASSIGNMENT FOR SESSION 4:

1. Scripture Memory: Study and complete the "Scripture Memory Instructions—Week Four" (page 28). Memorize the two verses on "Christ Paid the Penalty," Romans 5:8 and I Peter 3:18.
2. Quiet Time: Continue your Bible reading, marking, and recording.
3. Bible Study: Complete the "Relationship Evangelism Bible Study" (pages 29-31).
4. Evangelism: Come to class prepared to give your personal testimony without notes in less than four minutes.

Session 4

OUTLINE OF THIS SESSION:

1. Break into verse review groups and quote the two verses on "Christ Paid the Penalty," Romans 5:8 and 1 Peter 3:18. (Work at getting anything signed that you can on your *Completion Record*.)
2. Share some quiet time thoughts from your *Bible Reading Highlights Record*.
3. Have two or three people give a personal testimony without notes in less than four minutes.
4. Discuss the "Relationship Evangelism Bible Study" (pages 29-31).
5. Read the "Assignment for Session 5" (page 31).
6. Close in prayer.

Scripture Memory Instructions—Week Four

About the Verses

TOPIC 3. CHRIST PAID THE PENALTY

Either we must suffer the punishment for our sins and be separated from God throughout eternity, or someone else must pay the penalty so we can go free. Only Jesus Christ, the sinless, perfect God-man, could do this for us.

Romans 5:8—Paul said that God showed His great love for us by sending Christ to die in our place, even while we were still undeserving sinners. This is pure love and grace.

1 Peter 3:18—Peter told why Christ, the Righteous One, died for us, who are the unrighteous ones. He did it "to bring us to God"—to bridge the gulf that separated us from God's presence and fellowship.

On the cross God placed our sins on His Son. Jesus Christ bore our penalty, which is separation from the Father. That is why Jesus cried, "My God, my God, why have you forsaken me?" (Matthew 27:46). The Father had to turn away from His Son, because in that moment He was made sin for us. Now, instead of our sins, we have Christ's righteousness imparted to us, and we can enter the presence of God.

Your Weekly Plan

1. Place the next two verses (Romans 5:8 and 1 Peter 3:18) in the window of your pack.
2. Learn your new verses and review your memorized verses as you have done before, making sure to repeat all verses at least once each day.
3. Remember, always say the topic first, then the reference, the verse, and the reference again at the end.
4. By the end of the week check your new verses by writing them out from memory or quoting them to someone else.

RELATIONSHIP EVANGELISM BIBLE STUDY

TWO KEY INGREDIENTS

The Scriptures give us insight into how the gospel can have its greatest impact. There are two key ingredients: preaching (or proclaiming) the gospel, and affirming (or modeling) the gospel message through the life of a believer. This study will help you understand the scriptural basis for proclaiming and affirming.

PROCLAIMING THE GOSPEL

1. According to 2 Corinthians 5:18-20, with what have we, as Christians, been entrusted?

_____

_____

2. What are Christians commanded to do in Mark 16:15?

_____

_____

3. What does Paul see as his life purpose in Ephesians 3:7-8?

_____

_____

4. Write a brief summary of the Christian's responsibility in proclaiming the gospel from the above verses.

_____

_____

_____

In addition to proclaiming the gospel, the Christian is directed to affirm or display the reality of the Christian message in his or her own life. In this way the non-Christian not only hears but sees what it means to come into a relationship with Jesus Christ.

AFFIRMING THE GOSPEL

5. How does Christ instruct us to relate to the non-Christians around us? Matthew 5:13-16

_____

_____

6. In Philippians 2:14-15 how do our lives function in affirming the gospel?

_____

_____

_____

7. From the following verses list some of the ways we are to relate to non-Christians: Matthew 5:43-48; Luke 14:12-14; Colossians 4:5-6; 2 Corinthians 4:5.

_____

_____

_____

_____

_____

How do the above actions and attitudes affirm the gospel?

_____

_____

_____

_____

_____

8. From Matthew 9:10-13, explain how Jesus Christ related to unbelievers and what His purpose was.

_____

_____

9. Why is a relationship with a person necessary to affirm the gospel?

_____

_____

_____

THE PROCESS OF RELATIONSHIP EVANGELISM

> *"My food," said Jesus, "is to do the will of him who sent me and to finish his work. Do you not say, 'Four months more and then the harvest'? I tell you, open your eyes and look at the fields! They are ripe for harvest. Even now the reaper draws his wages, even now he harvests the crop for eternal life, so that the sower and the reaper may be glad together. Thus the saying 'One sows and another reaps' is true. I sent you to reap what you have not worked for. Others have done the hard work, and you have reaped the benefits of their labor."*
>
> —John 4:34-38

In John 4:34-38, seeing people come to Christ is equated with reaping a harvest; it is the final step in a series of activities. A harvest must be preceded by breaking up ground, sowing, watering, growth, and finally, reaping. Christ tells us that when we are involved in reaping (seeing someone come to Christ) much preliminary labor has already been done by others.

10. Before coming to Christ what are some literal ways that planting, watering, and growth might take place in a non-Christian's life? John 4:34-38

_____

_____

_____

_____

_____

11. In 1 Corinthians 3:5-9 Paul describes a real example of how planting, watering and growth took place.
    a. What does verse 8 say about the importance of sowing and reaping?

_____

_____

_____

    b. Who is responsible for growth? Verse 7

_____

_____

    c. What is the individual Christian's responsibility? Verses 5,8,9

_____

_____

SUMMARY

The Christian has been provided with two primary means to win the world to Christ: the message of the gospel and the reality of the gospel in the Christian's life. These two means are effective in reaching both the religious and the secular person. Relationship Evangelism is primarily the process of adapting the two means to the best advantage of the person we are seeking to lead to Christ. Relationship Evangelism is a process and its length will be determined to a great extent by how much or how little labor has been done before we enter into the picture with the individual. Nevertheless, the ultimate results of evangelism are dependent upon God who "gives the growth" and the individual who must, through an act of his will, voluntarily receive Christ as Savior and Lord.

ASSIGNMENT FOR SESSION 5:

1. Scripture Memory: Study and complete the "Scripture Memory Instructions—Week Five" (page 32). Memorize the two verses on "Salvation Not by Works," Ephesians 2:8-9 and Titus 3:5.
2. Quiet Time: Continue your Bible reading, marking, and recording.
3. Bible Study: Complete the Bible study, "Love in Action" (pages 33-37).
4. Evangelism: Come to class prepared to give your personal testimony without notes in less than four minutes.

Session 5

OUTLINE OF THIS SESSION:

1. Break into verse review groups and quote the two verses on "Salvation Not by Works," Ephesians 2:8-9 and Titus 3:5. (Work at getting anything signed that you can on your *Completion Record*.)
2. Share some quiet time thoughts from your *Bible Reading Highlights Record*.
3. Have two or three people give a personal testimony without notes in less than four minutes.
4. Discuss the Bible study, "Love in Action" (pages 33-37).
5. Read the "Assignment for Session 6" (page 37).
6. Close in prayer.

Scripture Memory Instructions—Week Five

About the Verse

TOPIC 4. SALVATION NOT BY WORKS

Most people have the idea that their eternal destiny will be decided by their good deeds being weighed against their bad ones. So they try to earn or solicit God's mercy by good and charitable acts that will blind Him to their faults.

Ephesians 2:8-9—Paul made it clear that salvation is not by our works, but only by God's grace— His unearned and unmerited favor. Salvation is a gift we receive by faith. If we could work for it, we could then boast that we had attained it, but God alone will receive the glory for saving us.

Titus 3:5—Here again Paul stated that we are not saved by our own efforts, but by God's merciful action. This is hard for some people to accept. It goes against a person's independent nature and "do-it-yourself" philosophy of life. To be saved means we are cleansed of our sins and born anew spiritually. This is a work of the Holy Spirit, who effects regeneration in us. He washes us clean.

Your Weekly Plan

1. Place the next two verses (Ephesians 2:8-9 and Titus 3:5) in the window of your verse pack.

2. Read the context of your new verses in your Bible to help you understand them in their setting.

3. If you haven't already done so, try working on your new verses during your morning quiet time, meditating on their meaning.

4. Strive for word perfection, and check your new verses by the end of the week by writing them out or quoting them to someone else.

LOVE IN ACTION

Today people have many different definitions of love. Most of these come from the illustrations of love found in movies, on television, in advertisements and magazines, and, perhaps, from personal experience. The Scriptures speak directly about love. The Bible tells us what love is, and how we may demonstrate it.

> **THINK ABOUT**: Generally what is the world's concept of love?

WHAT IS GENUINE LOVE?
1. How is love defined?
   a. Using a secular dictionary, define love.

   _____

   _____

   _____

   b. Using a Bible dictionary, define love.

   _____

   _____

   _____

   c. How do the two differ?

   _____

   _____

   _____

2. First Corinthians 13:4-8 gives some of the characteristics of Biblical love.
   a. Fill in the chart below.

WHAT LOVE IS	WHAT LOVE IS NOT

b. What are two or three major conclusions you can make about love based on this passage?

_____

_____

_____

_____

3. Carefully read 1 John 4:8-21.
   a. What important fact about God do you see in verse 8?

   _____

   _____

   b. What has God done to demonstrate His love for us?

   _____

   _____

   c. Because of God's love for us, what should our response be? Verses 11,19

   _____

   _____

   d. To what degree can love and fear exist together? Verse 18

   _____

   _____

THE FOCUS OF YOUR LOVE

4. From the passages you have studied, define love in your own words.

   _____

   _____

   _____

5. Read John 13:34-35.
   a. What is one of the surest evidences that you are a follower of Christ?

   _____

   _____

   b. Why do you think Jesus placed such emphasis on demonstrating love?

   _____

   _____

Love enters into our everyday actions in a variety of ways. Many people relate to others with only the tacit agreement: "If you do your part, I'll do mine." This conditional way of giving of ourselves is not love. God wants us to say, "I'll love you even if I receive nothing in return." It is this selfless giving and loving which God forms in our attitudes and actions.

LOVE IN HUMILITY

6. Humility comes from having the right perspective about God and yourself. What do the following verses tell you about your perspective toward God and toward yourself?

Jeremiah 9:23-24 _____

Philippians 2:3 _____

7. Read 1 Peter 5:5-6.
   a. What does the passage teach about humility?

   _____

   _____

   b. Why do you think God places such a high value on humility in a person's life?

   _____

   _____

8. Consider Romans 12:3.
   a. What error must you be careful to avoid?

   _____

   _____

   b. What are the results of overestimating yourself?

   _____

   _____

   c. What are the results of underestimating yourself?

   _____

   _____

   Both situations in this illustration are manifestations of pride, because the person is preoccupied with self.

PRIDE

Thinking too highly of self: "God's work can't get along without me!"	Thinking too lowly of self: "God can't do anything through me!"

9. Summarize the relationship between love and humility.

_____

_____

_____

LOVE IN SPEECH AND ACTION

10. Read Colossians 4:6 and write a paraphrase of the verse.

_____

_____

_____

_____

_____

11. God can give you gracious and loving words. What can the right words do?

Proverbs 12:25 _____

Proverbs 15:23 _____

Proverbs 16:24 _____

Proverbs 23:16 _____

Love is not merely an inner feeling, but also an act of the will. Love can be known only by the action it produces.

12. Read 1 John 3:16-18. Indicate how love can be demonstrated toward others.

_____

_____

_____

13. Make a list of some practical ways that you personally can demonstrate love toward these people:

Christians

_____

_____

_____

_____

Non-Christians

_____

_____

_____

_____

"To love the whole world
For me is no chore;
My only real problem's
My neighbor next door."

SUMMARY
Review the chapter subtopics and write your own summary of each section.

What is Genuine Love?

_____

_____

_____

_____

_____

_____

The Focus of Your Love

_____

_____

_____

_____

Love in Humility

_____

_____

_____

_____

_____

Love in Speech and Action

_____

_____

_____

_____

_____

ASSIGNMENT FOR SESSION 6:
1. Scripture Memory: Study and complete the "Scripture Memory Instructions—Week Six" (page 38). Memorize the verses on "Must Receive Christ", John 1:12 and Romans 10:9-10.
2. Quiet Time: Continue your Bible reading, marking and recording.
3. Bible Study: Complete the Bible study, "Purity of Life" (pages 39-44).

Session 6

OUTLINE OF THIS SESSION:

1. Break into verse review groups and quote the verses on "Must Receive Christ", John 1:12 and Romans 10:9-10.
2. Share some quiet time thoughts from your *Bible Reading Highlights Record.*
3. Discuss the Bible study, "Purity of Life" (pages 39-44).
4. Read the "Assignment for Session 7" (page 44).
5. Close in prayer.

Scripture Memory Instructions—Week Six

About the Verses

TOPIC 5. MUST RECEIVE CHRIST

The New Testament teaches that we are saved solely by believing in Jesus Christ. Nothing else is required. Today, *believe* often means merely to give mental assent. Many say, "Oh yes, I believe in God." But in the Bible belief means completely trusting and resolutely committing oneself to Jesus Christ as Savior from sin. Paul wrote, "For in the gospel a righteousness from God is revealed, a righteousness that is by faith from first to last, just as it is written: 'The righteous will live by faith'" (Romans 1:17). Faith in what the Bible says requires a positive action; believing means doing something. In your memory verses for this week, the importance of both believing and verbalizing that belief is stressed.

John 1:12—John equated receiving Jesus Christ with believing on Him. This is how one becomes a child of God. Everyone is familiar with the act of receiving a gift. One simply takes it and thanks the person who gave it, and then enjoys the gift.

Romans 10:9-10—There is a point in time when a person comes to know and believe the gospel. He or she understands the substitutionary death of Christ on the cross, the forgiveness of sin, and Christ's rightful ownership over his life. In his heart and mind he realizes, "I now understand what Christ did on the cross and I know He died for *me.*"

It is important for this person to confirm his faith in Christ by verbally acknowledging Christ as Savior and Lord. A practical way for him to do this is to 1) thank God in prayer for forgiveness and eternal life through Christ and 2) state clearly to another individual that he has believed in and accepted Christ's gospel.

Your Weekly Plan

1. Place John 1:12 and Romans 10:9-10 in the window of your verse pack.

2. By now you have learned the importance of starting promptly each week to learn a new verse on the very first day.

3. Learn your new verses and review your old ones as you have been doing.

4. At the end of the week check your new verses by writing them out or quoting them to someone else.

PURITY OF LIFE

It has been stated, "The new morality is nothing more than the old immorality in modern clothes." As society experiences moral decline, it becomes less popular for the Christian to take a stand on the moral absolutes of God's Word. Though freedom from all moral responsibility is sought by many people, Christians will only find God's greatest blessing by continuing to live by God's Word.

THINK ABOUT: Generally what does the world use as standards for evaluating morality?

GOD'S STANDARD

1. What is God's standard for purity? 1 Peter 1:15-16

_____

_____

_____

How do you think God expects us to live up to this standard?

_____

_____

_____

_____

2. What are some ways we are to demonstrate God's standard?

Matthew 5:21-22 _____

_____

Matthew 5:27-28 _____

_____

Romans 12:1-2 _____

_____

2 Corinthians 7:1 _____

_____

"Every man has a train of thought on which he rides when he is alone. The dignity and nobility of his life, as well as his happiness, depend upon the direction in which that train is going, the baggage it carries and the scenery through which it travels."

—Joseph Fort Newton

3. Study Colossians 1:21-23.
   a. What has God done to insure our holiness?

   _____

   _____

   b. What must we do?

   _____

   _____

THE IMPORTANCE OF PERSONAL PURITY

4. Read 1 Corinthians 6:13-20.
   a. List several reasons why we should avoid immorality.

   _____

   _____

   _____

   _____

   b. How do you think immoral behavior affects our relationship with God?

   _____

   _____

   _____

   c. How does it affect our relationship with others? (Consider both Christians and
      non-Christians.)

   _____

   _____

   _____

   _____

5. The world's standards differ greatly from God's. From 1 John 2:15-16, what are some characteristics of man which reflect the world's standards? List and define these on the chart below.

CHARACTERISTIC	DEFINITION

6. What do the Scriptures say to the following excuses for wrong moral behavior?
   a. "Since everyone else does it, it must be right."

   Proverbs 14:12 _____

   _____

   b. "I only need to discover what is right for me."

   Ecclesiastes 11:9 _____

   _____

   c. "Nobody will ever find out that I did it."

   Hebrews 4:13 _____

   _____

   d. "I'll stop after this one time."

   Galatians 6:7-8 _____

   _____

   e. "I didn't really *do* anything—all I did was *think* it."

   Matthew 5:28 _____

   _____

7. The battle for purity is fought in the mind. Read Romans 8:5-8.
   a. What two types of people are referred to in the passage?

   _____

   _____

   b. What are the results of each "mind-set"?

   _____

   _____

   _____

8. On what should we choose to focus our thoughts? Philippians 4:8

   _____

   _____

   Suggest some practical ways in which to motivate yourself to dwell on these things.

   _____

   _____

   _____

   _____

   _____

Try to forget the number 13. When you have forgotten it, check this box ☐. This is how some people try to avoid immorality—they think they can just make themselves not think about it. It is impossible to eliminate a wrong thought from your mind unless you substitute something good in its place. How might Scripture memory and meditation improve your thought life?

_____

_____

_____

_____

THE PATH TO PURITY

9. Read Ephesians 4:17-24.

   a. How does the passage describe the non-Christian's walk?

   _____

   _____

   _____

   _____

   b. What steps should Christians take to overcome their former way of life? Verses 22-24

   _____

   _____

   _____

   _____

   c. What are some practical ways to do this?

   _____

   _____

   _____

   _____

10. What can we do to live a clean life, pleasing to the Lord?

    Psalm 119:9-11 _____

    _____

    Proverbs 4:14-15 _____

    _____

    Romans 13:14 _____

    _____

    Galatians 5:16 _____

    _____

11. Study Genesis 39:7-12 and 2 Samuel 11:1-4. Compare the events in Joseph's and David's lives.

	JOSEPH	DAVID
a. What were the surrounding circumstances?		
b. What were their respective attitudes?		
c. What were their resulting actions?		

d. Why do you think these two men responded in different ways to a similar situation?

_____

_____

_____

_____

12. What Scriptural standards do you have concerning your relationship with the opposite sex? State two of them.

_____

_____

_____

_____

"Food was meant for the stomach and the stomach for food; but God has no permanent purpose for either. But you cannot say that our physical body was made for sexual promiscuity; it was made for God, and God is the answer to our deepest longings."

—1 Corinthians 6:13 (PH)

SUMMARY
Review the chapter subtopics and write your own summary of each section.

God's Standard

_____

_____

_____

_____

_____

_____

The Importance of Personal Purity

_____

_____

_____

_____

_____

_____

The Path to Purity

_____

_____

_____

_____

_____

_____

ASSIGNMENT FOR SESSION 7:
1. Scripture Memory: Study and complete the "Scripture Memory Instructions—Week Seven" (page 45). Memorize the verses on "Assurance of Salvation", 1 John 5:13 and John 5:24.
2. Quiet Time: Continue your Bible reading, marking, and recording.
3. Evangelism:
   a. Come to class prepared to give your personal testimony without notes in less than four minutes.
   b. Read the material on *The Bridge Illustration* (pages 46-51) and be prepared to discuss it in class.

Session 7

OUTLINE OF THIS SESSION:

1. Break into verse review groups and quote the verses on "Assurance of Salvation", 1 John 5:13 and John 5:24.
2. Share some quiet time thoughts from your *Bible Reading Highlights Record.*
3. Have two or three people give a personal testimony without notes in less than four minutes.
4. Discuss *The Bridge Illustration* (pages 46-51).
5. Read the "Assignment for Session 8" (page 51).
6. Close in prayer.

Scripture Memory Instructions—Week Seven

About the Verses

TOPIC 6. ASSURANCE OF SALVATION

It is impossible to build a solid structure on a shaky foundation. And it is impossible to grow in the Christian life properly if one is unsure of his salvation. Some Christians do not believe they can know they have eternal life. Others gauge the assurance of their salvation by their feelings, a most unstable foundation. But God wants us to *know* we have eternal life.

1 John 5:13—John stated clearly that his primary objective in this epistle was to help those who believe in Jesus Christ to know that they have eternal life.

But how can we know? One evidence is our desire to please God, resulting from the Holy Spirit's residence in our bodies. Other evidences of new life in Christ are the desires to read His Word, to commune with Him in prayer, to fellowship with other believers, and to tell others of Him. But the foundation on which all evidence rests is the promise of His Word.

John 5:24—Jesus said if we hear His Word and believe on the Father through Him, we have eternal life. This eternal life is a *present* possession. We will never have to stand judgment for our sins because the moment we believe, we pass from spiritual death to spiritual life. The primary basis for assurance of salvation is to believe what God says about it.

Your Weekly Plan

1. Place 1 John 5:13 and John 5:24 in the window of your pack. You will learn 1 John 5:13 in the first two days and John 5:24 the next two days.

2. Don't forget to review the new verses frequently each day and all the verses in your pack daily. If you get an early start and use spare moments during the day, you should have no difficulty reviewing 29 verses each day.

3. Remember to meditate on your verses and apply them to your life.

4. At the end of the week check your new verses by writing them out or quoting them to someone else.

The Bridge Illustration
How to Use "The Bridge" to Communicate the Gospel

The Bridge Illustration is one of many effective methods of presenting the gospel. It has been used successfully to communicate the gospel over many years and in many contexts, in groups and person-to-person. You will find it to be a useful and effective tool to aid you in sharing the gospel.

Many variations of *The Bridge Illustration* are in use. The presentation described here is one of the most commonly used variations. Your group leader may ask you to make adjustments in the format presented here in your workbook. Learn the method he or she presents, and become skilled in that method. After you have used this method to present the gospel to several non-Christians, you may also want to make a few adjustments in the format to make it more your own. This illustration will become a sharpened tool in your hands if these adjustments are based on actual experience in communicating the gospel.

FLEXIBILITY
The Bridge Illustration can take as little as 10 minutes to present, or it can be stretched out to an hour or more. A normal presentation will last 15 to 30 minutes. The flexibility of this presentation is one of its greatest assets. It can be tailored specifically to a person or situation.

SENSITIVITY
The way in which the Holy Spirit leads you to witness will vary in different situations. It is important to be observant and sensitive as you are relating to the person with whom you are sharing "The Bridge." In any type of ministry situation it is important to pray silently and ask God for guidance and wisdom, and for the ability to communicate the gospel clearly.

THE LEAD-IN
Experience has shown that it is helpful to have a few statements and questions in mind to help open the door for presenting the gospel. Often an ideal time to share the gospel is after a person has heard your personal testimony. You first want to get his response to your testimony by saying something like:

"Well, that's my story. What do you think?"

Or, "Well, that's my story. What is your reaction to what happened to me?" A more direct lead-in is: "How about you, Jim? Have you ever thought much about becoming a Christian?"

If there is time to talk further and the person still shows interest and capacity to hear more, you might say something like, "You know, Jim, there's a diagram that summarizes and clarifies what it means to be a real Christian and to know for certain that you have eternal life. If you have a few more minutes, may I sketch it out for you?" When he says, "Yes," you may proceed.

If you feel the person has heard as much as he can absorb at that time, you might say something like: "You know, Jim, there is a diagram that clarifies what it means to be a real Christian and to know for certain that you have eternal life. When you have 15 or 20 minutes sometime, why don't we sit down and I will sketch it out for you? OK?" Then, at a later date, you can get his consent to go through the illustration.

In many situations you will find it natural to ask permission to show the illustration without having given your testimony.

PRESENTATION

One of the most effective ways to present the gospel using *The Bridge Illustration* is to utilize questions about the Scriptures which will enable a person to see each truth directly from God's Word. You will need to convey four concepts as you draw out "The Bridge":

1. **God's Purpose**—*Abundant Life* John 10:10
   Eternal Life John 3:16
2. **Our Problem** —*All Have Sinned* Rom. 3:23 (Isaiah 53:6)
   Sin's Penalty Rom. 6:23; Heb. 9:27
3. **God's Remedy**—*Christ Paid the Penalty* Rom. 5:8; 1 Peter 3:18
   Salvation Not by Works Eph. 2:8-9 (Titus 3:5)
4. **Our Response**—*Must Receive Christ* John 1:12; Rom. 10:9-10
   Assurance of Salvation John 5:24 (1 John 5:13)

The diagrams on pages 47-50 show how your illustration will develop as you present it. The printed text shows how you can use questions to present this material. You should note that each segment is introduced by a transition statement, followed by one or more questions. After the person has had a chance to state his observations, you should clarify and summarize each point and then make the transition to the next passage.

GOD'S PURPOSE

Let's look at a couple Bible verses that tell us about some of God's purposes for us.

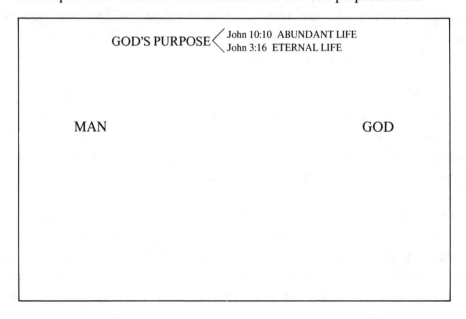

John 10:10. What does this passage indicate is one of God's purposes in sending His Son? He desires that we experience an abundant life. This would include such things as love, peace, purpose and fulfillment.

John 3:16. What additional purpose do you see for God sending us His Son? So then, from these statements we can say that God desires that we experience abundant life now, and eternal life (everlasting fellowship) with Him.

OUR PROBLEM

But we have a problem. God did not create us like a robot who would automatically love and have fellowship with Him in return. He gave us a will and the freedom of choice. Let's look at what people are like—apart from God.

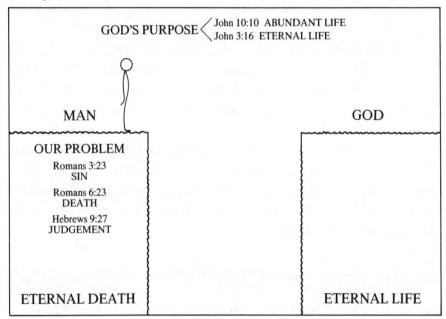

Romans 3:23. What does this verse say about all people? Does this include me? Does this include you? How would you describe sin according to this verse? Have you ever wondered what effect our sin has? Let's look at some other passages.

Romans 6:23. How would you define wages? That's right, something in payment for the work you do. According to this verse, what payment can we expect for the sin (wrong) we have done? Do you think this death is physical, spiritual, or what? (At this point, you will need to clarify that death is referring to spiritual death. See John 3:18). If we die physically, and also die spiritually, the consequence or payment resulting from our sin is eternal death (separation from God).

Hebrews 9:27. What is one thing death brings with it? You can see by this statement that each of us will die physically, and after we die physically we will face judgment. So we can see that when we look at the condition of a person apart from God, it isn't very encouraging. We have sinned, and the penalty of sin is eternal death (separation from God). Also we see that the consequences of our sin bring about the judgment of God. We genuinely are separated from God.

GOD'S REMEDY

In spite of the fact that we have turned our backs on God and have disobeyed Him, He has provided a remedy so that we can know Him personally. He wants to give us both abundant life and eternal life. Only one bridge can cross the gulf that exists between a person and God, and that bridge is Jesus Christ, through His death on the cross.

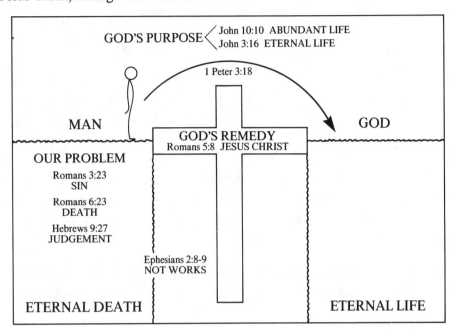

Romans 5:8. Did God want us to become worthy before He provided a solution? What did God's love cause Him to do? People use many approaches in trying to find favor with God and to secure eternal life.

Ephesians 2:8-9. What does the Bible teach regarding salvation and our efforts to be good? What is one reason God won't accept our good deeds as payment for our sins? (At this point you might also want to explain that a penalty of "eternal death" could not be removed by anything less.) Let's look at another passage that explains this further.

1 Peter 3:18. (You should explain this passage phrase by phrase so that the gospel is clearly covered. This is an excellent verse to emphasize the good news of Christ's Resurrection.)

OUR RESPONSE

Real belief results in a response on our part. Christ has made it possible for us to cross over to God's side and experience the full life He wants us to have. But we are not automatically on God's side.

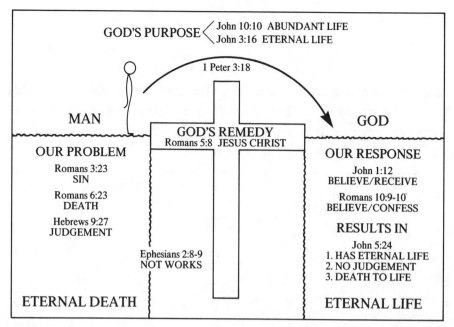

John 1:12. What does this passage equate with believing? What does receiving Christ mean to you? (At this point, clarify that believing and receiving involve our mind, our emotions [desire], and our will.) A verse which can be used to illustrate how a person might express his faith and belief that Jesus is his Savior is:

Romans 10:9-10. What two things does this passage say are necessary for salvation? If you respond in this way, of what can you be assured? Let me summarize the illustration with a very important verse.

John 5:24. What two things must we do according to this statement? What three results does Jesus promise to those who believe in Him? God does not want us to wonder if we have eternal life. He wants us to be sure. The Bible says, "I write these things to you who believe in the name of the Son of God so that you may know that you have eternal life." (1 John 5:13)

PERSONAL INVITATION

Assume that you have been sharing the gospel with Susan. You might use the following suggestions to help her move toward a personal commitment.

1. "Does this make sense to you?"
2. "Do you have any questions about it?"
3. "Where would you place yourself in this illustration?"
   a. If Susan says, "On God's side," you might ask when she received Christ. Ask her to relate the specifics of her experience in receiving Christ.
   b. If she points to the left side or to the chasm, inquire, "What would you have to believe to be on God's side?" See if she can clearly communicate the issues of the gospel and the necessity of believing on Christ. You might say, "Is there any reason why you shouldn't cross over to God's side and be certain of eternal life?"
4. If she indicates a responsiveness to the gospel, ask, "Would you like to trust in (receive) Jesus Christ now? If so, I would be happy to pray with you."
5. If you believe she understands the gospel but is not yet ready to commit her life to Christ,

encourage her to give these things further thought and consideration. Be sure, in a few days, to talk with her about the gospel and/or get her involved in some type of an investigative Bible study.

6. Whatever response she has, be sure she understands what she would specifically pray to affirm her faith in Christ. It is as simple as A-B-C:

A—Acknowledge your sin and be willing to turn from it.

B—Believe Christ died for your sins and rose again.

C—Commit your life to Christ as Savior and Lord.

Note that these 3 points correspond to:

A—Our Problem

B—God's Remedy

C—Our Response

PRACTICAL SUGGESTIONS

1. Do not memorize *The Bridge Illustration*. Learn the principles, ideas, verses, and key sentences. Make it your own.

2. Make an outline of the presentation as you would like to give it, and practice giving it to another Christian.

3. Learn the questions suggested here. But equally important, think through each passage and develop your own questions.

4. Draw the illustration as you talk. This is an attention-getter.

5. Use a Bible rather than quoting verses. Have the non-Christian read them out of the Bible.

6. If the non-Christian brings up objections during your presentation, you might say, "That's a good question. For the sake of continuity, may I try to answer that after completing the illustration?"

7. The ultimate goal is to bring a person to salvation in Christ. Proceed as far as the Holy Spirit gives you freedom. If the non-Christian is open to receive Christ, then have him pray.

In the following weeks, you will be asked to present *The Bridge Illustration* three times.

First, you will present the *outline* of *The Bridge Illustration* to *another member* of your 2:7 group.

Second, you will present *The Bridge Illustration* in a *role playing* situation to another member of your 2:7 group.

Third, you will present *The Bridge Illustration* to *someone outside* of your 2:7 group.

ASSIGNMENT FOR SESSION 8:

1. Scripture Memory: Review all the verses memorized in Course 2.

2. Quiet Time: Continue your Bible reading, marking and recording.

3. Bible Study: Complete the Bible study, "Integrity in Living" (pages 52-56).

4. Evangelism:

a. Come to class prepared to give your personal testimony without notes in less than four minutes.

b. Prepare to draw the outline (verses and main points) of *The Bridge Illustration* for another member of the class.

Session 8

OUTLINE OF THIS SESSION:
1. Break into verse review groups and work on getting anything signed that you can on your *Completion Record.*
2. Share some quiet time thoughts from your *Bible Reading Highlights Record.*
3. Have two or three people give a personal testimony without notes in less than four minutes.
4. Discuss the progress you are making with non-Christians.
5. Break into groups of two and take turns presenting *The Bridge Illustration* outline.
6. Discuss the Bible study, "Integrity in Living" (pages 52-56).
7. Read the "Assignment for Session 9" (pages 56-57).
8. Close in prayer.

INTEGRITY IN LIVING

We must each deal daily with issues of right versus wrong—good versus evil. When struggling with these issues, we often tend to rationalize our behavior and compromise God's standards of integrity. Often these sins are explained away or ignored. These are the "vices of the virtuous"—sins which may have become accepted as the normal standard. But we must not allow any compromise with sin to infiltrate our lives.

THINK ABOUT: How do you feel about "little white lies"?

THE STRUGGLE FOR INTEGRITY
Integrity is defined as being of sound moral principle; consistently upright, honest and sincere.

1. Describe the natural condition of our hearts. Jeremiah 17:9

_____

_____

_____

2. What are some of the ways we can be deceived?

James 1:22 _____

1 John 1:8 _____

Romans 16:17-18 _____

Ephesians 4:14 _____

2 Corinthians 11:3-4 _____

3. Saul, the first king of Israel, is a good example of a man who lacked personal integrity. Read 1Samuel 15:1-23.

a. What was Saul commanded to do? Verses 1-3

_____

_____

_____

b. What did he do? Verse 9

_____

_____

_____

c. How did he try to justify his disobedience? Verses 13-21

_____

_____

_____

d. How did God view the situation? Verses 22-23

_____

_____

_____

_____

4. A hypocrite is a person who pretends to be what he is not. Study Mark 7:6-8 and list what Jesus says about hypocrites and give an example of each.

THE HYPOCRITE	EXAMPLE

LIVING A LIFE OF INTEGRITY

  5. Read 1 Thessalonians 2:3-11

    How did the Apostle Paul demonstrate a life of integrity?

    a. By speech

_____

_____

    b. By deed

_____

_____

    c. Through motives

_____

_____

  6. Read 1 Timothy 3:1-9.

    a. Which qualities required of a person seeking church office have to do with integrity?

_____

_____

    b. Are these qualities only for church leaders, or for everyone to attain? Explain your answer.

_____

_____

  7. List the qualities of a person of integrity from Psalm 15:1-5.

_____

_____

_____

    Which of these qualities do you think are most violated among the people with whom you associate? Consider both Christians and non-Christians.

_____

_____

_____

_____

  8. Integrity needs to be displayed in all aspects of our lives.

    a. List below some of the areas where integrity tends to be neglected.

      Romans 13:6-7 _____

      Ephesians 5:22 _____

      Ephesians 5:25 _____

      Ephesians 6:1 _____

Colossians 3:23-24 _____

1 Peter 2:13-14 _____

b. Is there ever a time when integrity toward God would override our commitment to these areas of responsibility? See Acts 4:18-20 and 5:27-29.

_____

_____

_____

THE CONSCIENCE—AN AID TO INTEGRITY

9. How does the dictionary define "conscience"?

_____

_____

_____

10. From the following passages, describe the conscience.

1 Corinthians 8:7-12 _____

1 Timothy 3:9 _____

1 Timothy 4:2 _____

Titus 1:15 _____

Hebrews 10:22 _____

1 Peter 3:16, 21 _____

11. Read Acts 24:16.
    a. What were Paul's objectives regarding his conscience?

_____

_____

_____

_____

b. How can we develop or maintain this kind of conscience?

Toward God _____

_____

Toward Man _____

_____

SUMMARY

Review the chapter subtopics and write your own summary of each section on the next page.

The Struggle for Integrity

_____

_____

_____

_____

_____

_____

_____

_____

Living a Life of Integrity

_____

_____

_____

_____

_____

_____

_____

_____

_____

The Conscience—An Aid to Integrity

_____

_____

_____

_____

_____

_____

_____

_____

ASSIGNMENT FOR SESSION 9:
   1. Scripture Memory: Work on any requirements not yet completed.
   2. Quiet Time: Continue your Bible reading, marking and recording.

3. Evangelism:
   a. Come to class prepared to give your personal testimony without notes in less than four minutes.
   b. Prepare to present *The Bridge Illustration* to another member of the class in a role playing situation.
4. Other:
   a. Study and complete "Verse Analysis of Matthew 6:33" (pages 58-61).
   b. Study and complete "Priorities—Part I" (pages 61-65).

Session 9

OUTLINE OF THIS SESSION:

1. Break into review groups and work on getting anything signed that you can on your *Completion Record*.
2. Share some quiet time thoughts from your *Bible Reading Highlights Record*.
3. In groups of two, take turns role playing *The Bridge Illustration*.
4. Have two or three people give a personal testimony without notes in less than four minutes.
5. Discuss "Verse Analysis of Matthew 6:33" (pages 58-61).
6. Discuss "Priorities—Part I" (pages 61-65).
7. Read the "Assignment for Session 10" (page 65).
8. Close in prayer regarding your priorities.

Verse Analysis of Matthew 6:33
Preparation for a Discussion on Priorities

This study is foundational for the discussion on priorities in Sessions 9-10. After reading the context of Matthew 6:33 aloud twice, you will take these steps to analyze it:

1. Paraphrase the verse
2. Study the context
3. Find cross-references
4. Write down real or potential problems
5. Make a personal application

☐ I have read Matthew 6:19-34 aloud twice. (Check when completed.)

1. PARAPHRASE.

Paraphrase Matthew 6:33 in your own words. Consult the translations in the box on the following page to stimulate your thinking.

_____

_____

_____

_____

_____
_____
_____
_____
_____
_____
_____

> "But seek first his kingdom and his righteousness, and all these things will be given to you as well" (NIV).
>
> "But seek first the kingdom of God and His righteousness, and all these things shall be added to you" (NKJV).
>
> "But seek first His kingdom and His righteousness; and all these things shall be added to you" (NASB).
>
> "Set your hearts on his kingdom first, and on his righteousness, and all these other things will be given you as well" (JB).
>
> "But seek for (aim at and strive after) first of all His kingdom, and His righteousness [His way of doing and being right], and then all these things taken together will be given you besides" (AMP).

2. CONTEXT.

Summarize the key thoughts in Matthew 6:25-32, and 6:34. Do *not* include verse 33.

_____
_____
_____
_____
_____
_____
_____
_____
_____
_____
_____
_____
_____

3. CROSS-REFERENCES.

What is the thought contained in the following verses that is similar to Matthew 6:33?

Deuteronomy 28:2 _____

_____

2 Chronicles 26:5 _____

_____

2 Chronicles 31:20-21 _____

_____

Psalm 84:11 _____

_____

4. PROBLEMS.

a. Define *righteousness* and *kingdom of God* in the following spaces. You will want to use a dictionary, Bible dictionary, encyclopedia, or commentary in preparing your definitions. You may need to check with your church library or with a friend who has these resource books.

Righteousness _____

_____

_____

_____

_____

_____

Kingdom of God _____

_____

_____

_____

_____

_____

_____

b. What do you feel is the implication of the word *seek?*

_____

_____

_____

_____

c. This verse opens with the word *but*. As you compare verse 33 with verses 31-32, what contrast does the word *but* imply?

_____

_____

_____

_____

5. APPLICATION.

What is one application of Matthew 6:33 that you can make to your own life?

_____

_____

_____

_____

_____

_____

_____

_____

_____

_____

_____

_____

Priorities—Part I

Priorities have to do with order and importance. A priority list includes things in order of their importance.

Why do we feel one thing is more important than another? It depends on what we want and what we would like to accomplish—what our goals and desires are. We all have goals and desires and these influence our choices.

A Christian's priorities should be based on God's will for his or her life as revealed in the Scriptures. Jesus Christ gave us the injunction, "But seek first his kingdom and his righteousness" (Matthew 6:33). That which pertains to God's kingdom has priority over our physical needs according to the context of the Sermon on the Mount.

To have the right priorities, we must have the right goals. From the following passages, write the goals and desires these godly men had or exhorted others to have.

- David (Psalm 27:4) _____

_____

- Joshua (Joshua 24:15) _____

  _____

- Jesus (John 4:34) _____

  _____

- Paul (Romans 12:2) _____

  _____

- Paul (Colossians 1:28-29) _____

  _____

- John (3 John 4) _____

  _____

As committed Christians, we should "imitate their faith."

> *"Remember your leaders, who spoke the word of God to you. Consider the outcome of their way of life and imitate their faith."*
>
> —Hebrews 13:7

GOALS

The goals for our lives, on which our priorities should be based, can be divided into two areas: (1) what we are to *be*—growing in Christlikeness (Romans 8:29) and (2) what we are to *do*—grow in effective service (Galatians 6:9-10).

Christlikeness

Make a list of the characteristics of Christlikeness from the following passages (use a translation, not a paraphrase):

GALATIANS 5:22-23	MATTHEW 5:3-10
1. _____	1. _____
2. _____	2. _____
3. _____	3. _____
4. _____	4. _____
5. _____	5. _____
6. _____	6. _____
7. _____	7. _____
8. _____	8. _____
9. _____	

Make a list of what you feel are the five most important characteristics of Christlikeness from the preceding lists:

1. _____   4. _____

2. _____   5. _____

3. _____

Serving

Serving means helping at the point of need. This may mean offering aid or advice; it could also mean admonishing a friend, sharing the gospel, or helping someone memorize Scripture.

There are many ways in which we may serve others. Match the principles with the Scripture references:

_____ Mark 9:41   1. Doing humble tasks for God's children.

_____ John 13:14-16   2. Caring for widows.

_____ Acts 6:1-3   3. Helping meet material or finanical needs.

_____ Ephesians 4:12   4. Praying for others.

_____ Ephesians 6:5-7   5. Building up other Christians.

_____ Colossians 4:12   6. Being thorough and hardworking on the job.

_____ 1 Timothy 5:17   7. Giving a drink of cold water.

_____ 1 John 3:17-18   8. Preaching and teaching the Word of God.

The greatest service you can render to people is to bring them into a right relationship with Jesus Christ. This could be helping someone come to salvation in Christ, or ministering to the spiritual development of a Christian.

"Seeking the kingdom of God first" has to do with glorifying God in the lives of individuals. So your highest concern in serving Christ is to minister to spiritual needs, and then to other needs which they may have. At times it might be necessary to minister to the material or physical needs before you can minister to spiritual needs.

GUIDELINES FOR SETTING AND APPLYING PRIORITIES

1. **Make responsible choices.** Many of life's choices are already made for us: by Scripture (God), parents, government and physical limitations. But whenever we have options, we are responsible to make choices. Slaves had little power of choice, yet in the first century the gospel spread rapidly among them.

2. **Be decisive.** One of the greatest hindrances to doing God's will is a lack of planning. Most of us have about 40 unplanned hours a week where we must choose how we will use that time. Take time to plan prayerfully with Matthew 6:33 as your guide. For example, plan how you will use a free evening or a Saturday or Sunday afternoon.

3. **Plan ahead.** The following approach can sharpen your effectiveness:
   a. Make one list of things you need to do, and another list of things you want to do.
   b. Pray for sensitivity from the Holy Spirit as you evaluate your lists.
   c. Number the items (1, 2, 3, etc.) in the order of their importance.
   d. Do item 1. Then do item 2, and so on through your list. Your list will need to be revised periodically because of a steady stream of new demands and opportunities. Many people make a new list every morning.

4. **Persevere.** Determination and perseverance are two necessary ingredients for living according to priorities. The flesh will often rebel against doing what you should do. Paul said, "I beat my body and make it my slave" (1 Corinthians 9:27). In other words, he is saying, "I make it do what it should do, not what it wants to do."

5. **Acknowledge dependence on God.** While we acknowledge that determination and perseverance are necessary ingredients for living by priorities, we must also acknowledge that God must give blessing and grace for our efforts to really count (see 2 Corinthians 3:5; John 15:5; Zechariah 4:6). God is our enabler!

6. **Be adaptable.** In the book of James we are taught that when we have made our plans, we must learn to say, "If the Lord wills, we will carry them out" (see James 4:13-16). God sometimes has plans for us of which we know nothing. His thoughts are higher than our thoughts (see Isaiah 55:9), so don't get "bent out of shape" when interruptions come, but rather submit to Him with thanksgiving in all your circumstances (see Romans 8:28; Psalm 115:3).

7. **Don't be easily swayed.** Some people will try to control our lives. At one point in His ministry people were trying to make plans for Christ (see Luke 4:42-44), but He would not submit to them. He said He had to do what His Father sent him to do. Knowing what God wants you to do will enable you to discern when to submit to the desires of well-meaning people and when to say "no" graciously.

8. **Review your goals.** In order to improve in making right choices based on God's goals for our lives, we must often reconsider these goals and evaluate whether we are making right choices. Human nature tends to lead us away from our goals. A half day alone with God regularly is excellent for helping keep us on target.

9. **Prioritize.** Working by priority does not mean you will get everything done that you would like to. It does mean you will get the most important things done. Jesus said, "I have brought you [God the Father] glory on earth by completing the work you gave me to do" (John 17:4). Yet, there was much more He could have done. Let us learn from Jesus' example—live by God's priorities for our lives and commit to Him the things we are unable to do.

CONCLUSION

Sometimes priorities are based on selfish desires. The flesh tends to make it difficult for us to relate our priorities to God's plan for our lives, because that involves sacrifice.

Do you want God to be "first" in your life? Then working on His purposes and priorities will be a lifelong process. Don't be discouraged when you fail, but instead make periodic evaluations, such as regularly spending a half day in prayer and thinking. Remember the Lord's admonition, "Seek FIRST His Kingdom!"

ASSIGNMENT FOR SESSION 10:
1. Scripture Memory: Continue reviewing your verses and work on any requirements not yet completed.
2. Quiet Time: Continue your Bible reading, marking and recording.
3. Evangelism:
    a. Come to class prepared to give your personal testimony without notes in less than four minutes.
    b. Present *The Bridge Illustration* to another person outside of your 2:7 group. Be prepared next week to tell about it.
4. Other: Read and be prepared to discuss "Priorities—Part II" (pages 66-70).

Session 10

OUTLINE OF THIS SESSION:

1. Break into verse review groups and work on getting anything signed that you can on your *Completion Record*.
2. Share some quiet time thoughts from your *Bible Reading Highlights Record*.
3. Have two or three people give a personal testimony without notes in less than four minutes.
4. Discuss your experience in presenting *The Bridge Illustration* to someone outside the group.
5. Discuss "Priorities—Part II" (pages 66-70).
6. Read the "Assignment for Session 11" (page 70).
7. Close in prayer.

Priorities—Part II

THE PRIORITY OF GOD

"An unmarried man is concerned about the Lord's affairs—how he can please the Lord. But a married man is concerned about the affairs of this world—how he can please his wife" (1 Corinthians 7:32-33).

For every Christian, whether single or married, God must be the first priority. E. M. Bounds' classic statement, "To be little with God is to be little for God," captures the idea of this priority. We spend time with God because He greatly desires our fellowship. He longs to be with us, for we are "the kind of worshipers the Father seeks" (John 4:23). In His presence we grow in godliness and the reality of our relationship with God becomes apparent to those around us. "When they saw the courage of Peter and John and realized that they were unschooled, ordinary men, they were astonished and they took note that these men had been with Jesus" (Acts 4:13).

Occasionally larger blocks of time with God should supplement your regular devotional times. Become strong in your grasp of the Word of God through Scripture memory and Bible study. Pray regularly that God will give you wisdom in applying the Word to your life. If you have a grasp on the great truths of the Bible, you will frequently find yourself in places of effective ministry. In time, your life will touch the lives of many.

The triangle diagram shows that the closer two individuals are to God, the closer they will be to each other. This is true between husband and wife, between parent and child—between any two Christians. Therefore, as

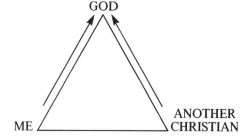

you pursue God Himself, you will reap relational benefits as well as personal benefits. Put your walk with God first! "As for me, it is good to be near God. I have made the Sovereign LORD my refuge" (Psalm 73:28). "The LORD is near to all who call on him, to all who call on him in truth. He fulfills the desires of those who fear him" (Psalm 145:18-19).

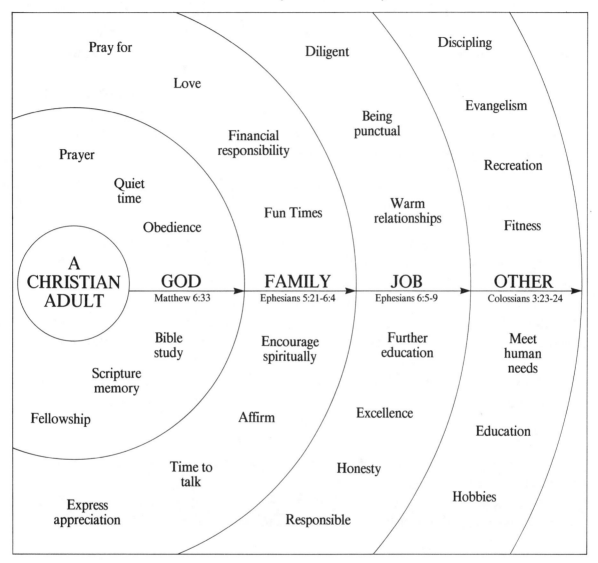

CIRCLES OF PRIORITY

The above illustration, "Circles of Priority," is a visual representation of our common areas of responsibility in life. The inner circles are of higher priority. Yet, you will want to work toward balance in all areas of life right from the beginning.

God has given each of us basic responsibilities we must not neglect. Ultimately you will determine in your own heart and mind what is priority for you in a given week or on a given day. We must give priority tasks and relationships extra weight when planning and scheduling our time.

Before we can be significantly effective for Christ, we must be spending consistent, meaningful time with God. He is to be our first priority (Matthew 6:33). "He has showed you, O man, what is good. And what does the LORD require of you? To act justly and to love mercy and to walk humbly with your God" (Micah 6:8).

THE PRIORITY OF FAMILY

The best springboard for a great influence for Christ in the lives of many people may be simply sharing the biblical principles that work in your marriage or in raising your children.

Credibility in the family must precede expansion of spiritual influence. "If anyone does not know how to manage his own family, how can he take care of God's church?" (1 Timothy 3:5) Not that you must have everything in order in every dimension of your family life, but you must be giving a high priority to getting your own house in order. Your home will become either a springboard to greater ministry or a millstone around your neck.

"For I have chosen him, so that he will direct his children and his household after him to keep the way of the LORD by doing what is right and just, so that the LORD will bring about for Abraham what he has promised him" (Genesis 18:19). Because of Abraham's faithfulness in the management of his family, God was able to prosper him spiritually.

Husband or Wife

Having a close vital relationship with God increases the probability of having a close vital relationship with your spouse. And having a good relationship in your marriage increases the probability of having a good relationship with your child. Priority does not imply neglect. It implies emphasis. Continue to work on your marriage.

Wives. Are you praying for your husband? Are you helping him to become more and more the leader and decision-maker he should be? Are you adapting to him? Are you a student of your husband, learning his moods, likes and dislikes, and strengths and weaknesses? Do you support and encourage him in what he feels led to pursue in life?

Husbands. Are you praying for your wife? Are you lifting your share of the load in household responsibilities and with the children? Have you read a book, listened to a tape, or seen a Christian film lately to sharpen your parenting skills? Are you and your wife thinking and planning together? Would your wife say you talk and pray together often enough? How often do you say, "Thank you?" Are you helping to meet your wife's spiritual, physical, and emotional needs as well as the financial ones?

You will have your greatest effectiveness in furthering the purposes of God in the world if you put your relationship to God first and give your spouse the strong second priority.

Children.

Whether you are married or find yourself in the situation of being a single parent, you will agree that your children are both an unbelievable blessing and an incredible responsibility. However, we live in a most opportune time in history. The Christian sector has a proliferation of books, tapes, and seminars on how to raise children. Many pastors and Christian counselors are experienced and trained to assist us through some of the more difficult struggles. We must allow time to acquire the necessary knowledge and skills and have the courage to seek sound advice or counseling when needed.

We want to avoid bypassing our children for "the ministry." We may find that we have not prepared our children for the opportunities and difficulties of life or helped them become disciples of Jesus Christ. When children are younger we may need to decrease our involvement in ministry— realizing that our own children represent a very high ministry priority.

Single Adults.

If you are a single adult, you have special benefits and advantages that enable you to make a significant contribution to what God desires to accomplish in the world today.

A large segment of the adult population is single. Single people are often more mobile and flexible in where they can live and what they can do. They have more time for Bible intake and spiritual growth than many married people. They usually are less hindered in reaching out to others and in pursuing spiritual and general personal development. This, however, is not true for a single parent with the important opportunity and responsibility of caring for children.

How much further education should you pursue? How much time with friends, neighbors, or roommates? What kind of ministry load can you carry and still have time off and avoid excessive pressure and stress? God can lead you, so make these issues a matter of prayer and give adequate time for planning and evaluation.

Invest your single life wisely! Become all that God wants you to be and use the leverage of your situation to make your impact for Christ. God may lead you to get married one day, or He may best be able to work in and through you if you remain single. Your responsibility is to follow Christ wholeheartedly and to trust Him for a fulfilling and significant future.

THE PRIORITY OF JOB

Your secular job takes up many hours each week. But it is a place where you can use your God-given skills and abilities. It supplies funds which can be invested to further the cause of Jesus Christ, as well as finances to meet your personal and family needs.

The job can also be your point of contact and friendship with a number of non-Christians who may come to Christ and become disciples. You should do your ministering, of course, without using "company time". Your work needs to be done "heartily as to the Lord," and so provide an open door for ministry as well as a source of provision and a sense of accomplishment.

THE PRIORITY OF CHURCH

Being a part of a local assembly of believers is most important! It is a place for both spiritual intake and ministry output.

Teaching a class of adults, young people, or children can be both a ministry and a context within which you can grow in your ability to motivate others and to communicate biblical truth clearly.

There are numerous opportunities to grow and minister. Pray for God's leading. Plan to be both taking in and giving out as you meet with other believers each week.

MINISTRY AND OTHER PRIORITIES

In *Growing Strong in God's Family* and during these first two courses of *The 2:7 Series*, there has been a persistent emphasis on the importance of relating to non-Christians, identifying with Christ, and then sharing your testimony and/or the gospel. Ministry has to be a solid part of the lifestyle of every believer if we hope to ever impact the world significantly for Christ. An increasing number of biblically sound churches are seeing the importance of ministering to physical and emotional as well as spiritual needs. There are limitless possibilities for ministry for every lay person. Some of the finest traditional and innovative ministries are being carried out by people who are *not* on the staff of a local church. They are "regular" Christian people with a job and perhaps a home and family. Plan to invest a portion of your energies in spreading the gospel, helping people become disciples, and in meeting human needs.

Are you reading books, listening to tapes, and enjoying a hobby? These are activities that can help make us sharper and more interesting to be around. Could further education perhaps help make you more effective in your job? Are you attending Christian or job-related seminars and conferences when they are available? We don't want to hit a plateau in life somewhere in our 30's, 40's or beyond.

Are you getting adequate exercise and sufficient time for rest and recreation? We need to give adequate attention to the care and welfare of our bodies and emotions as well as to our spiritual lives and ministries.

ASSIGNMENT FOR SESSION 11:
1. *Scripture Memory*: Work on getting any final memory requirements completed.
2. *Quiet Time*: Continue your Bible reading, marking, and recording.
3. *Bible Study*: Complete the Bible study, "Character in Action" (pages 71-76).

Session 11

OUTLINE OF THIS SESSION:
1. Break into verse review groups, and get anything signed that you can on your *Completion Record*.
2. Share some quiet time thoughts from your *Bible Reading Highlights Record*.
3. Discuss the Bible study, "Character in Action" (pages 71-76).
4. Review what you have learned in *Growing Strong in God's Family* and the first two courses of *The 2:7 Series* by reading aloud "Keep On Keeping On" (pages 76-77).
5. Close in prayer.

CHARACTER IN ACTION

A Christian is not immune to the harsh realities of human life. Sickness, sorrow, death, and other forms of pain and suffering are experienced by all people. But for a Christian, trials and suffering carry with it the promise of God's loving presence and sovereign purpose in shaping the inner qualities of life.

> **THINK ABOUT**: Why do you think God allows Christians to experience trials and suffering?

GOD'S ULTIMATE CONTROL
1. The Scriptures tell us that God is all powerful (omnipotent), all knowing (omniscient), and everywhere present (omnipresent).
   a. Read Psalm 139:1-16 and summarize God's involvement with you in the following areas:

   God's knowledge of me. Verses 1-6

   _____

   _____

   _____

God's presence with me. Verses 7-12

_____

_____

_____

God's development of me. Verses 13-16

_____

_____

_____

   b. What was the response of the psalmist to the knowledge of God's influence in his life?

     Verses 17-18 _____

_____

     Verses 23-24 _____

_____

2. What do the following verses teach about God's perspective and purpose?

   Isaiah 45:5-7 _____

_____

   Isaiah 46:9-10 _____

_____

   Romans 8:28 _____

_____

TRIALS AND SUFFERING PRODUCE CHARACTER

3. Read James 1:2-4, 12.

   a. How should a person respond to trials?

_____

_____

   b. What are the results of properly responding to trials?

_____

_____

4. In Romans 5:3-5, Paul says we are to exult (rejoice, glory) in our tribulations.

   a. What does tribulation produce in the Christian's life?

_____

_____

_____

b. Is it important that Paul mentioned these areas in a particular sequence? Why or why not?

_____

_____

5. How did the following men deal with adversity?

Joseph (Genesis 50:20) _____

_____

Job (Job 1:13-22) _____

_____

Shadrach, Meshach, Abednego (Daniel 3:13-18) ____

_____

The Apostles (Acts 5:40-42) _____

_____

Paul (Philippians 1:12-21) _____

_____

What impresses you most from these examples?

_____

_____

6. What are some of the reasons God tested the people of Israel? Deuteronomy 8:1-3, 16.

_____

_____

RESPONSE TO TRIALS AND SUFFERING

7. Sometimes the suffering we go through is a result of God's discipline. Read Hebrews 12;4-11.
   a. Why does God discipline us?

   _____

   _____

   _____

   b. What are the results of God's discipline?

   _____

   _____

   c. How do you think you can tell the difference between the discipline of God and the attack of Satan?

   _____

   _____

8. Though trials and suffering are difficult at the time, what are some positive aspects to consider?

Romans 8:18 _____

_____

2 Corinthians 1:3-4 _____

_____

1 Peter 5:10 _____

_____

Can you think of other positive aspects of suffering?

_____

_____

_____

9. Read Ephesians 5:20 and 1 Thessalonians 5:18.
   a. How does God want us to respond to every situation (including trials and suffering)?

   _____

   _____

   b. Why is this response important?

   _____

   _____

   _____

A person's response to problems determines his maturity level. Each crisis is an opportunity for victory or defeat.

PROBLEM ⟶ RESPONSE ⟶ VICTORY
                        OR
                     ⟶ DEFEAT

10. Think back over a specific trial or suffering you have gone through and consider the questions below:
    a. How did you respond to it?

    _____

    _____

    _____

    b. How could you have responded better?

    _____

    _____

    _____

c. Did you thank God for the circumstance?

_____

_____

_____

d. How did God use it in your life?

_____

_____

_____

e. Have you been able to use it to comfort someone else?

_____

_____

_____

> *When God wants to drill a man*
> *And thrill a man*
> *And skill a man.*
> *When God wants to mold a man*
> *To play the noblest part;*
> *When He yearns with all His heart*
> *To create so great and bold a man*
> *That all the world shall be amazed,*
> *Watch His methods, watch His ways!*
> *How He ruthlessly perfects*
> *Whom He royally elects!*
> *How He hammers him and hurts him,*
> *And with mighty blows converts him*
> *Into trial shapes of clay which*
> *Only God understands;*
> *While his tortured heart is crying*
> *And he lifts beseeching hands!*
> *How He bends but never breaks*
> *When his good He undertakes;*
> *How He uses whom He chooses*
> *And with every purpose fuses him;*
> *By every act induces him*
> *To try His splendor out—*
> *God knows what He's about!*
> —Anonymous

SUMMARY

Review the chapter subtopics and write your own summary of each section.

God's Ultimate Control

_____

_____

_____

_____

_____

Trials and Suffering Produce Character

_____

_____

_____

_____

_____

Response to Trials and Suffering

_____

_____

_____

_____

_____

Keep On Keeping On

WHAT YOU HAVE ACCOMPLISHED

You have now completed *The Growing Disciple* (the first two courses in *The 2:7 Series*), as well as *Growing Strong in God's Family*. Your diligence has brought you through significant steps in growing as a true disciple of Jesus Christ. Your Christian life and ministry have been enhanced by:

- Regularity in Scripture memory—you have now memorized 29 verses.
- Regularity in your quiet time—you are reading, marking, and recording Scripture on a daily basis.
- Regularity in Bible study—you have completed 17 topical lessons in question-and-answer type Bible study.
- Presentation of your personal testimony, which you have written out and are able to give in under four minutes.

- Praying conversationally and knowing how to spend extended time with God in a half day of prayer.
- Being confronted with, submitting to, and living under the lordship of Christ.
- Learning how to meditate on the Scriptures.
- Learning how to recognize and set priorities in your life.

FREE CERTIFICATE OF COMPLETION

As you reach this significant milestone, THE NAVIGATORS WOULD LIKE TO SEND YOU A CERTIFICATE OF COMPLETION FREE OF CHARGE. Complete the form below and mail to: The Navigators, Church Discipleship Ministries, P.O. Box 6000, Colorado Springs, CO 80934. (Your 2:7 leader may collect this information from each of you and send it in for your whole group.)

Please send me a certificate of completion for "The Growing Disciple" segment, which I will complete _____
                                  (Date)

Name _____
Address _____
Telephone _____
Church _____
Church address _____

Also, when you complete Course 5, The Navigators make available a certificate of completion and a small remembrance to honor your achievement.

Congratulations! You have persevered. You deserve to be recognized for work well done!

"The desire accomplished is sweet to the soul."

—Proverbs 13:19 (KJV)

THE MINISTERING DISCIPLE SERIES

The emphasis of *Growing Strong in God's Family* and Courses 1 and 2 in *The 2:7 Series* has been to strengthen the foundation of your Christian life and to sharpen your basic ministry skills.

The focus of Courses 3-5 in *The 2:7 Series* is to help you develop in ministry effectiveness. *The Ministering Disciple* is the title given to these three courses.

You will want to further your training by continuing into Course 3. This course will help you to maintain a close walk with God as well as to learn new and practical principles for effective ministry. You will:

- Learn how to be skilled as a small group Bible study leader.
- Learn how to organize and lead an Investigative Bible study with non-Christians.
- Memorize 12 key verses on *Rely on God's Resources*.
- Learn how to answer questions about the gospel.
- Experience another meaningful half day of prayer.
- Learn principles of spiritual multiplication.

Notes

PAGE	SOURCE

24   *Knight's Book of Illustrations* (Chicago: Moody Press, 1970).

25   J. Oswald Sanders, *Spiritual Leadership* (Chicago: Moody Press, 1967).

36   *Knight's Book of Illustrations* (Chicago: Moody Press, 1970).

39   *The Marriage Affair*, J. Allan Petersen, editor (Wheaton, Illinois: Tyndale House Publishers, 1971).

BIBLE READING HIGHLIGHTS RECORD

"Happy are those who keep My ways. Hear instruction and be wise, and do not refuse it. Happy is the man listening to Me, watching daily at My gates, keeping watch at My doorposts."

Proverbs 8:32-34, BERK

*Translation*_____ *Year*_____

○ **Sunday**   Date_____ All I read today_____
Best thing I marked today: *Reference:*_____
*Thought:*_____
_____
_____
_____
How it impressed me:_____
_____
_____
_____
_____
_____
_____
_____

○ **Monday**   Date_____ All I read today_____
Best thing I marked today: *Reference:*_____
*Thought:*_____
_____
_____
How it impressed me:_____
_____
_____
_____
_____
_____
_____
_____

○ **Tuesday**   Date_____ All I read today_____
Best thing I marked today: *Reference:*_____
*Thought:*_____
_____
_____
How it impressed me:_____
_____
_____
_____
_____

○ **Wednesday** Date_____ All I read today_____
Best thing I marked today: *Reference:*_____
*Thought:*_____
_____
_____
_____
How it impressed me:_____
_____
_____
_____
_____
_____
_____
_____
_____

○ **Thursday**   Date_____ All I read today_____
Best thing I marked today: *Reference:*_____
*Thought:*_____
_____
_____
_____
How it impressed me:_____
_____
_____
_____
_____
_____
_____

○ **Friday**   Date_____ All I read today_____
Best thing I marked today: *Reference:*_____
*Thought:*_____
_____
_____
How it impressed me:_____
_____
_____
_____
_____
_____
_____

○ **Saturday**   Date_____ All I read today_____
Best thing I marked today: *Reference:*_____
*Thought:*_____
_____
_____
How it impressed me:_____
_____
_____
_____
_____

BIBLE READING HIGHLIGHTS RECORD

"Happy are those who keep My ways. Hear instruction and be wise, and do not refuse it. Happy is the man listening to Me, watching daily at My gates, keeping watch at My doorposts."

Proverbs 8:32-34, BERK

Translation_____ Year_____

Sunday   Date_____ All I read today_____
Best thing I marked today: *Reference:*_____
Thought: _____
_____
_____
_____
How it impressed me:_____
_____
_____
_____
_____
_____
_____
_____

Monday   Date_____ All I read today_____
Best thing I marked today: *Reference:*_____
Thought: _____
_____
_____
_____
How it impressed me:_____
_____
_____
_____
_____
_____
_____
_____

Tuesday   Date_____ All I read today_____
Best thing I marked today: *Reference:*_____
Thought: _____
_____
_____
_____
How it impressed me:_____
_____
_____
_____
_____
_____

Wednesday Date_____ All I read today_____
Best thing I marked today: *Reference:*_____
Thought: _____
_____
_____
_____
How it impressed me:_____
_____
_____
_____
_____
_____
_____
_____
_____
_____

Thursday Date_____ All I read today_____
Best thing I marked today: *Reference:*_____
Thought: _____
_____
_____
_____
How it impressed me:_____
_____
_____
_____
_____
_____
_____

Friday   Date_____ All I read today_____
Best thing I marked today: *Reference:*_____
Thought: _____
_____
_____
_____
How it impressed me:_____
_____
_____
_____
_____
_____
_____
_____

Saturday   Date_____ All I read today_____
Best thing I marked today: *Reference:*_____
Thought: _____
_____
_____
_____
How it impressed me:_____
_____
_____
_____
_____

BIBLE READING HIGHLIGHTS RECORD

"Happy are those who keep My ways. Hear instruction and be wise, and do not refuse it. Happy is the man listening to Me, watching daily at My gates, keeping watch at My doorposts."

Proverbs 8:32-34, BERK

*Translation*_____ *Year*_____

○ **Sunday** Date_____ All I read today_____
Best thing I marked today: *Reference:*_____
*Thought:*_____
_____
_____
How it impressed me:_____
_____
_____
_____
_____
_____
_____

○ **Monday** Date_____ All I read today_____
Best thing I marked today: *Reference:*_____
*Thought:*_____
_____
_____
How it impressed me:_____
_____
_____
_____
_____
_____
_____

○ **Tuesday** Date_____ All I read today_____
Best thing I marked today: *Reference:*_____
*Thought:*_____
_____
_____
How it impressed me:_____
_____
_____
_____
_____
_____
_____

○ **Wednesday** Date_____ All I read today_____
Best thing I marked today: *Reference:*_____
*Thought:*_____
_____
_____
_____
How it impressed me:_____
_____
_____
_____
_____
_____
_____
_____
_____
_____

○ **Thursday** Date_____ All I read today_____
Best thing I marked today: *Reference:*_____
*Thought:*_____
_____
_____
How it impressed me:_____
_____
_____
_____
_____
_____
_____

○ **Friday** Date_____ All I read today_____
Best thing I marked today: *Reference:*_____
*Thought:*_____
_____
_____
How it impressed me:_____
_____
_____
_____
_____

○ **Saturday** Date_____ All I read today_____
Best thing I marked today: *Reference:*_____
*Thought:*_____
_____
_____
How it impressed me:_____
_____
_____
_____
_____
_____

BIBLE READING HIGHLIGHTS RECORD

"Happy are those who keep My ways. Hear instruction and be wise, and do not refuse it. Happy is the man listening to Me, watching daily at My gates, keeping watch at My doorposts."

Proverbs 8:32-34, BERK

Translation_____ Year _____

○ **Sunday**   Date_____ All I read today_____
Best thing I marked today: *Reference:*_____
Thought: _____
_____
_____
How it impressed me:_____
_____
_____
_____
_____
_____
_____
_____
_____

○ **Monday**   Date_____ All I read today_____
Best thing I marked today: *Reference:*_____
Thought: _____
_____
_____
How it impressed me:_____
_____
_____
_____
_____
_____
_____
_____

○ **Tuesday**   Date_____ All I read today_____
Best thing I marked today: *Reference:*_____
Thought: _____
_____
_____
How it impressed me:_____
_____
_____
_____
_____
_____

○ **Wednesday** Date_____ All I read today_____
Best thing I marked today: *Reference:*_____
Thought: _____
_____
_____
How it impressed me:_____
_____
_____
_____
_____
_____
_____
_____
_____
_____
_____

○ **Thursday**   Date_____ All I read today_____
Best thing I marked today: *Reference:*_____
Thought: _____
_____
_____
How it impressed me:_____
_____
_____
_____
_____
_____
_____
_____

○ **Friday**   Date_____ All I read today_____
Best thing I marked today: *Reference:*_____
Thought: _____
_____
_____
How it impressed me:_____
_____
_____
_____
_____
_____
_____
_____

○ **Saturday**   Date_____ All I read today_____
Best thing I marked today: *Reference:*_____
Thought: _____
_____
_____
How it impressed me:_____
_____
_____
_____
_____
_____

BIBLE READING HIGHLIGHTS RECORD

"Happy are those who keep My ways. Hear instruction and be wise, and do not refuse it. Happy is the man listening to Me, watching daily at My gates, keeping watch at My doorposts."

Proverbs 8:32-34, BERK

*Translation*_____ *Year*_____

○ **Sunday**   Date_____ All I read today_____
Best thing I marked today: *Reference:*_____
Thought: _____
_____
_____

How it impressed me:_____
_____
_____
_____
_____
_____
_____
_____

○ **Monday**   Date_____ All I read today_____
Best thing I marked today: *Reference:*_____
Thought: _____
_____
_____

How it impressed me:_____
_____
_____
_____
_____
_____
_____
_____

○ **Tuesday**   Date_____ All I read today_____
Best thing I marked today: *Reference:*_____
Thought: _____
_____
_____

How it impressed me:_____
_____
_____
_____
_____
_____
_____

○ **Wednesday** Date_____ All I read today_____
Best thing I marked today: *Reference:*_____
Thought: _____
_____
_____

How it impressed me:_____
_____
_____
_____
_____
_____
_____
_____
_____
_____
_____

○ **Thursday**   Date_____ All I read today_____
Best thing I marked today: *Reference:*_____
Thought: _____
_____
_____

How it impressed me:_____
_____
_____
_____
_____
_____
_____
_____

○ **Friday**   Date_____ All I read today_____
Best thing I marked today: *Reference:*_____
Thought: _____
_____
_____

How it impressed me:_____
_____
_____
_____
_____
_____
_____
_____

○ **Saturday**   Date_____ All I read today_____
Best thing I marked today: *Reference:*_____
Thought: _____
_____
_____

How it impressed me:_____
_____
_____
_____
_____
_____
_____

BIBLE READING HIGHLIGHTS RECORD

"Happy are those who keep My ways. Hear instruction and be wise, and do not refuse it. Happy is the man listening to Me, watching daily at My gates, keeping watch at My doorposts."

Proverbs 8:32-34, BERK

Translation_____ Year _____

Sunday   Date_____ All I read today_____
Best thing I marked today: *Reference:*_____
Thought: _____
_____
_____
_____
How it impressed me:_____
_____
_____
_____
_____
_____
_____

Monday   Date_____ All I read today_____
Best thing I marked today: *Reference:*_____
Thought: _____
_____
_____
How it impressed me:_____
_____
_____
_____
_____
_____
_____

Tuesday   Date_____ All I read today_____
Best thing I marked today: *Reference:*_____
Thought: _____
_____
_____
How it impressed me:_____
_____
_____
_____
_____
_____

Wednesday Date_____ All I read today_____
Best thing I marked today: *Reference:*_____
Thought: _____
_____
_____
_____
How it impressed me:_____
_____
_____
_____
_____
_____
_____
_____
_____
_____

Thursday   Date_____ All I read today_____
Best thing I marked today: *Reference:*_____
Thought: _____
_____
_____
How it impressed me:_____
_____
_____
_____
_____
_____
_____
_____

Friday   Date_____ All I read today_____
Best thing I marked today: *Reference:*_____
Thought: _____
_____
_____
How it impressed me:_____
_____
_____
_____
_____
_____

Saturday   Date_____ All I read today_____
Best thing I marked today: *Reference:*_____
Thought: _____
_____
_____
How it impressed me:_____
_____
_____
_____
_____

BIBLE READING HIGHLIGHTS RECORD

"Happy are those who keep My ways. Hear instruction and be wise, and do not refuse it. Happy is the man listening to Me, watching daily at My gates, keeping watch at My doorposts."

Proverbs 8:32-34, BERK

*Translation*_____ *Year* _____

○ **Sunday**　Date_____ All I read today_____
Best thing I marked today: *Reference:*_____
Thought: _____
_____
_____
_____

How it impressed me:_____
_____
_____
_____
_____
_____
_____
_____
_____

○ **Monday**　Date_____ All I read today_____
Best thing I marked today: *Reference:*_____
Thought: _____
_____
_____
_____

How it impressed me:_____
_____
_____
_____
_____
_____
_____
_____
_____

○ **Tuesday**　Date_____ All I read today_____
Best thing I marked today: *Reference:*_____
Thought: _____
_____
_____
_____

How it impressed me:_____
_____
_____
_____
_____
_____
_____

○ **Wednesday** Date_____ All I read today_____
Best thing I marked today: *Reference:*_____
Thought: _____
_____
_____
_____

How it impressed me:_____
_____
_____
_____
_____
_____
_____
_____
_____
_____
_____

○ **Thursday**　Date_____ All I read today_____
Best thing I marked today: *Reference:*_____
Thought: _____
_____
_____
_____

How it impressed me:_____
_____
_____
_____
_____
_____
_____
_____
_____

○ **Friday**　Date_____ All I read today_____
Best thing I marked today: *Reference:*_____
Thought: _____
_____
_____
_____

How it impressed me:_____
_____
_____
_____
_____
_____
_____
_____
_____

○ **Saturday**　Date_____ All I read today_____
Best thing I marked today: *Reference:*_____
Thought: _____
_____
_____
_____

How it impressed me:_____
_____
_____
_____
_____
_____
_____

BIBLE READING HIGHLIGHTS RECORD

"Happy are those who keep My ways. Hear instruction and be wise, and do not refuse it. Happy is the man listening to Me, watching daily at My gates, keeping watch at My doorposts."

Proverbs 8:32-34, BERK

*Translation*_____ *Year* _____

○ **Sunday**   Date_____ All I read today_____
Best thing I marked today: *Reference:*_____
Thought: _____
_____
_____
_____
How it impressed me:_____
_____
_____
_____
_____
_____
_____
_____

○ **Monday**   Date_____ All I read today_____
Best thing I marked today: *Reference:*_____
Thought: _____
_____
_____
_____
How it impressed me:_____
_____
_____
_____
_____
_____
_____
_____

○ **Tuesday**   Date_____ All I read today_____
Best thing I marked today: *Reference:*_____
Thought: _____
_____
_____
_____
How it impressed me:_____
_____
_____
_____
_____

○ **Wednesday** Date_____ All I read today_____
Best thing I marked today: *Reference:*_____
Thought: _____
_____
_____
_____
How it impressed me:_____
_____
_____
_____
_____
_____
_____
_____
_____

○ **Thursday**   Date_____ All I read today_____
Best thing I marked today: *Reference:*_____
Thought: _____
_____
_____
_____
How it impressed me:_____
_____
_____
_____
_____
_____
_____
_____

○ **Friday**   Date_____ All I read today_____
Best thing I marked today: *Reference:*_____
Thought: _____
_____
_____
_____
How it impressed me:_____
_____
_____
_____
_____
_____
_____

○ **Saturday**   Date_____ All I read today_____
Best thing I marked today: *Reference:*_____
Thought: _____
_____
_____
_____
How it impressed me:_____
_____
_____
_____
_____

BIBLE READING HIGHLIGHTS RECORD

"Happy are those who keep My ways. Hear instruction and be wise, and do not refuse it. Happy is the man listening to Me, watching daily at My gates, keeping watch at My doorposts."

Proverbs 8:32-34, BERK

*Translation*_____ *Year* _____

○ **Sunday** Date_____ All I read today_____
Best thing I marked today: *Reference:*_____
Thought: _____
_____
_____
_____
How it impressed me:_____
_____
_____
_____
_____
_____
_____
_____

○ **Monday** Date_____ All I read today_____
Best thing I marked today: *Reference:*_____
Thought: _____
_____
_____
How it impressed me:_____
_____
_____
_____
_____
_____
_____
_____
_____

○ **Tuesday** Date_____ All I read today_____
Best thing I marked today: *Reference:*_____
Thought: _____
_____
_____
How it impressed me:_____
_____
_____
_____
_____

○ **Wednesday** Date_____ All I read today_____
Best thing I marked today: *Reference:*_____
Thought: _____
_____
_____
How it impressed me:_____
_____
_____
_____
_____
_____
_____
_____
_____

○ **Thursday** Date_____ All I read today_____
Best thing I marked today: *Reference:*_____
Thought: _____
_____
_____
How it impressed me:_____
_____
_____
_____
_____
_____
_____
_____

○ **Friday** Date_____ All I read today_____
Best thing I marked today: *Reference:*_____
Thought: _____
_____
_____
How it impressed me:_____
_____
_____
_____
_____
_____
_____
_____
_____

○ **Saturday** Date_____ All I read today_____
Best thing I marked today: *Reference:*_____
Thought: _____
_____
_____
How it impressed me:_____
_____
_____
_____
_____

BIBLE READING HIGHLIGHTS RECORD

"Happy are those who keep My ways. Hear instruction and be wise, and do not refuse it. Happy is the man listening to Me, watching daily at My gates, keeping watch at My doorposts."

Proverbs 8:32-34, BERK

*Translation*_____ *Year*_____

○ **Sunday** Date_____ All I read today_____
Best thing I marked today: *Reference:*_____
*Thought:*_____
_____
_____
How it impressed me:_____
_____
_____
_____
_____
_____

○ **Monday** Date_____ All I read today_____
Best thing I marked today: *Reference:*_____
*Thought:*_____
_____
_____
How it impressed me:_____
_____
_____
_____
_____
_____

○ **Tuesday** Date_____ All I read today_____
Best thing I marked today: *Reference:*_____
*Thought:*_____
_____
_____
How it impressed me:_____
_____
_____
_____
_____
_____

○ **Wednesday** Date_____ All I read today_____
Best thing I marked today: *Reference:*_____
*Thought:*_____
_____
_____
_____
How it impressed me:_____
_____
_____
_____
_____
_____
_____
_____

○ **Thursday** Date_____ All I read today_____
Best thing I marked today: *Reference:*_____
*Thought:*_____
_____
_____
How it impressed me:_____
_____
_____
_____
_____
_____

○ **Friday** Date_____ All I read today_____
Best thing I marked today: *Reference:*_____
*Thought:*_____
_____
_____
How it impressed me:_____
_____
_____
_____
_____
_____

○ **Saturday** Date_____ All I read today_____
Best thing I marked today: *Reference:*_____
*Thought:*_____
_____
_____
How it impressed me:_____
_____
_____
_____
_____

BIBLE READING HIGHLIGHTS RECORD

"Happy are those who keep My ways. Hear instruction and be wise, and do not refuse it. Happy is the man listening to Me, watching daily at My gates, keeping watch at My doorposts."

Proverbs 8:32-34, BERK

Translation_____ Year _____

○ **Sunday** Date_____ All I read today_____
Best thing I marked today: *Reference:*_____
Thought: _____
_____
_____
How it impressed me:_____
_____
_____
_____
_____
_____

○ **Monday** Date_____ All I read today_____
Best thing I marked today: *Reference:*_____
Thought: _____
_____
_____
_____
How it impressed me:_____
_____
_____
_____
_____
_____
_____

○ **Tuesday** Date_____ All I read today_____
Best thing I marked today: *Reference:*_____
Thought: _____
_____
_____
How it impressed me:_____
_____
_____
_____
_____
_____

○ **Wednesday** Date_____ All I read today_____
Best thing I marked today: *Reference:*_____
Thought: _____
_____
_____
_____
How it impressed me:_____
_____
_____
_____
_____
_____
_____
_____
_____

○ **Thursday** Date_____ All I read today_____
Best thing I marked today: *Reference:*_____
Thought: _____
_____
_____
How it impressed me:_____
_____
_____
_____
_____
_____

○ **Friday** Date_____ All I read today_____
Best thing I marked today: *Reference:*_____
Thought: _____
_____
_____
How it impressed me:_____
_____
_____
_____
_____
_____
_____

○ **Saturday** Date_____ All I read today_____
Best thing I marked today: *Reference:*_____
Thought: _____
_____
_____
How it impressed me:_____
_____
_____
_____
_____
_____

BIBLE READING HIGHLIGHTS RECORD

"Happy are those who keep My ways. Hear instruction and be wise, and do not refuse it. Happy is the man listening to Me, watching daily at My gates, keeping watch at My doorposts."

Proverbs 8:32-34, BERK

Translation_____ Year _____

◯ **Sunday**   Date_____ All I read today_____
Best thing I marked today: *Reference:*_____
Thought: _____
_____
_____
_____
How it impressed me:_____
_____
_____
_____
_____
_____
_____
_____

◯ **Monday**   Date_____ All I read today_____
Best thing I marked today: *Reference:*_____
Thought: _____
_____
_____
How it impressed me:_____
_____
_____
_____
_____
_____
_____
_____
_____

◯ **Tuesday**   Date_____ All I read today_____
Best thing I marked today: *Reference:*_____
Thought: _____
_____
_____
How it impressed me:_____
_____
_____
_____
_____
_____
_____

◯ **Wednesday** Date_____ All I read today_____
Best thing I marked today: *Reference:*_____
Thought: _____
_____
_____
_____
How it impressed me:_____
_____
_____
_____
_____
_____
_____
_____
_____

◯ **Thursday**   Date_____ All I read today_____
Best thing I marked today: *Reference:*_____
Thought: _____
_____
_____
How it impressed me:_____
_____
_____
_____
_____
_____
_____
_____
_____

◯ **Friday**   Date_____ All I read today_____
Best thing I marked today: *Reference:*_____
Thought: _____
_____
_____
How it impressed me:_____
_____
_____
_____
_____
_____
_____

◯ **Saturday**   Date_____ All I read today_____
Best thing I marked today: *Reference:*_____
Thought: _____
_____
_____
How it impressed me:_____
_____
_____
_____
_____
_____

BIBLE READING HIGHLIGHTS RECORD

"Happy are those who keep My ways. Hear instruction and be wise, and do not refuse it. Happy is the man listening to Me, watching daily at My gates, keeping watch at My doorposts."

Proverbs 8:32-34, BERK

Translation_____ Year _____

Sunday Date_____ All I read today_____
Best thing I marked today: *Reference:*_____
Thought: _____
_____
_____
How it impressed me:_____
_____
_____
_____
_____
_____
_____

Monday Date_____ All I read today_____
Best thing I marked today: *Reference:*_____
Thought: _____
_____
How it impressed me:_____
_____
_____
_____
_____
_____
_____
_____

Tuesday Date_____ All I read today_____
Best thing I marked today: *Reference:*_____
Thought: _____
_____
How it impressed me:_____
_____
_____
_____
_____
_____

Wednesday Date_____ All I read today_____
Best thing I marked today: *Reference:*_____
Thought: _____
_____
_____
How it impressed me:_____
_____
_____
_____
_____
_____
_____
_____

Thursday Date_____ All I read today_____
Best thing I marked today: *Reference:*_____
Thought: _____
_____
How it impressed me:_____
_____
_____
_____
_____
_____

Friday Date_____ All I read today_____
Best thing I marked today: *Reference:*_____
Thought: _____
_____
How it impressed me:_____
_____
_____
_____
_____
_____

Saturday Date_____ All I read today_____
Best thing I marked today: *Reference:*_____
Thought: _____
_____
How it impressed me:_____
_____
_____
_____

BIBLE READING HIGHLIGHTS RECORD

"Happy are those who keep My ways. Hear instruction and be wise, and do not refuse it. Happy is the man listening to Me, watching daily at My gates, keeping watch at My doorposts."

Proverbs 8:32-34, BERK

Translation_____ Year _____

Sunday Date_____ All I read today_____
Best thing I marked today: *Reference:*_____
*Thought:*_____
_____
_____
How it impressed me:_____
_____
_____
_____
_____
_____
_____

Monday Date_____ All I read today_____
Best thing I marked today: *Reference:*_____
*Thought:*_____
_____
How it impressed me:_____
_____
_____
_____
_____
_____
_____
_____
_____

Tuesday Date_____ All I read today_____
Best thing I marked today: *Reference:*_____
*Thought:*_____
_____
How it impressed me:_____
_____
_____
_____
_____
_____
_____

Wednesday Date_____ All I read today_____
Best thing I marked today: *Reference:*_____
*Thought:*_____
_____
_____
_____
How it impressed me:_____
_____
_____
_____
_____
_____
_____
_____
_____
_____
_____

Thursday Date_____ All I read today_____
Best thing I marked today: *Reference:*_____
*Thought:*_____
_____
_____
How it impressed me:_____
_____
_____
_____
_____
_____
_____

Friday Date_____ All I read today_____
Best thing I marked today: *Reference:*_____
*Thought:*_____
_____
_____
How it impressed me:_____
_____
_____
_____
_____

Saturday Date_____ All I read today_____
Best thing I marked today: *Reference:*_____
*Thought:*_____
_____
How it impressed me:_____
_____
_____
_____
_____
_____

Prayer Sheet

REQUEST	GOD'S ANSWER

Prayer Sheet

REQUEST	GOD'S ANSWER

Prayer Sheet

REQUEST	GOD'S ANSWER

Prayer Sheet

REQUEST	GOD'S ANSWER